INTELLIGENCE TESTS

Published by SevenOaks

Copyright © 2016 Carlton Books Limited

10 9 8 7 6 5 4 3 2 1

Text and puzzle content copyright © 1996, 1998, 2010
British Mensa Limited
Design and artwork copyright © 1996, 1998, 2010
Carlton Books Limited

A CIP catalogue record for this book is available from the
British Library

ISBN 978-1-78177-587-5

Printed and bound by CPI Group (UK) Ltd, Croydon, CR0 4YY

The content of this book was previously published in *The
Complete Book of Intelligence Tests*, *Boost Your IQ* and *Improve
Your Mind Power*

INTELLIGENCE TESTS

Includes intelligence tests, puzzles and advice for maximizing your brain-power

Allen · Fulton · Gale · Skitt

SEVENOAKS

WHAT IS MENSA?

Mensa is the international society for people with a high IQ.
We have more than 100,000 members in over 40 countries worldwide.

The society's aims are:
   to identify and foster human intelligence for the benefit of humanity
   to encourage research in the nature, characteristics, and uses of intelligence
   to provide a stimulating intellectual and social environment for its members

Anyone with an IQ score in the top two per cent of the population is eligible to
become a member of Mensa – are you the 'one in 50' we've been looking for?

Mensa membership offers an excellent range of benefits:
   Networking and social activities nationally and around the world
   Special Interest Groups – hundreds of chances to pursue your hobbies
      and interests – from art to zoology!
   Monthly members' magazine and regional newsletters
   Local meetings – from games challenges to food and drink
   National and international weekend gatherings and conferences
   Intellectually stimulating lectures and seminars
   Access to the worldwide SIGHT network for travellers and hosts

For more information about Mensa: www.mensa.org, or

British Mensa Ltd.,
St John's House,
St John's Square,
Wolverhampton
WV2 4AH
Telephone: +44 (0) 1902 772771

CONTENTS

About Intelligence	6
Test One	50
Test Two	66
Test Three	84
Test Four	102
Test Five	120
Test Six	136
Test Seven	152
Maximize Your Memory	168
Reading Skills	209
Understanding Numbers	228
Increase Your Intelligence	249
Test Eight	262
Test Nine	280
Test Ten	296
Test Eleven	312
Test Twelve	328
Test Thirteen	346
Test Fourteen	362
Test Bonanza	378

Intelligence has many definitions. In 1923 it was wryly defined by the psychologist Edwin Boring as "That quality which intelligence tests measure." And things are exactly as simple and as complex as that. IQ — our intelligence quotient — is a difficult thing to pin down. IQ tests are scorned by some as testing only the ability to do IQ tests, but many of the abilities involved in the completion of IQ tests have proven to be very useful in our daily lives. The various abilities of logical thinking, problem solving, dealing with the language that we use every day, and manipulating numbers and shapes are the same abilities which, when combined with emotional reasoning, make us effective human beings.

Another psychologist, Ulric Neisser, recently defined intelligence around the concept of an *ideal prototype* with people being more or less intelligent according to how closely they approach the prototype. There are two ways of achieving a prototype. The psychometric prototype is statistical where we simply say that a perfect score is 1 and this becomes the ideal prototype. We are scored according to our deviation from that score. This is close to the method used to score most IQ tests currently in use where the IQ score is the deviation of a person's score on a test from the mean test score of a reference

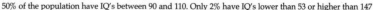

50% of the population have IQ's between 90 and 110. Only 2% have IQ's lower than 53 or higher than 147

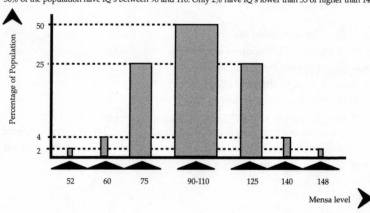

population, divided by the standard deviation. In other words, the rating which you achieve on an IQ test is compared with the rating which everyone else achieves, and your score is weighted according to the results of others. By definition according to the convention of scoring, the average IQ is 100, and we know that fifty percent of the population will score between 90 and 110. But if, on a particular test, it were found that the average of all tested was 90, the weighting would be adjusted to bring the average back up to 100. Thus are tests standardized. Looking at the sample figures on the last page it can be seen that if all points were plotted, the classic bell-shaped curve would be evident. More on that later.

The other way of achieving a prototype is to define the ideal intelligence in terms of cognitive-psychology, where intelligence is viewed as a process. To do this we would have to choose the ideal processes of intelligence such as problem definition, memory storage, mental imaging, resource collection, and problem solving, and we would also have the dilemma of having to define the ideal prototype use for that intelligence. But the processes are complex and infinitely varied according to the type of problem being solved and we can be specific only to the environment in which we operate. Solving the problem of (say) stopping somebody from shouting at you involves few of the processes of defining the difference between (say) paper and metal foil. As to environments, a physics genius may have the ideal intelligence for making discoveries about relativity or quantum mechanics, but be unable to survive in a desert where the average nomad who has never heard of physics thrives happily. But take the nomad out of the desert into a physics laboratory and the situation is reversed.

Perhaps with something like the above example in mind, intelligence has been defined by H. Woodrow as "The capacity to acquire capacity"; by S.S. Colvin as "The ability to adjust oneself to the environment"; and by R. Pintner as "The ability to adapt oneself adequately to relatively new situations in life." In other words, if the nomad is an intelligent nomad, he will be able to learn about physics, given the opportunity and inclination, and if the physics professor finds himself in the desert, if he is an intelligent physics professor and comes under the instruction of a group of nomads, he will be able to learn the things necessary for survival.

Types of intelligence

What Woodrow, Colvin and Pintner all seem to be identifying has come to be known as *fluid intelligence* — the combination of qualities measured by the Cattell test used by Mensa, and the same qualities which have ensured our survival as a species and the lack of which causes the downfall of species less able to adapt to changing circumstances. This combined intelligence aspect has great relevance in everyday life, particularly in today's changing jobmarket. Versatility is the most important asset of potential employees. What you are capable of now matters more than what you have done in the past. There have been a number of cases where very high fliers have been enticed away, for huge sums of money, from jobs where they were achieving spectacular success. It was hoped that they could bring that success with them and turn failing businesses into successes, but they became equally spectacular failures in their new positions. Where did things go wrong? Why cannot future success be measured by past performance?

The answer is that it may have taken years for them to learn how to be good at their last job, and during those years they will have accumulated judgement, wisdom, and thinking skills specific to that job and situation. But in the case of those somewhat lacking in fluid intelligence, only specific to that situation. Their new employers have failed to realize that someone who has spent the last twenty years learning about (say) steel may have achieved that success by hard work and determination and by learning the hard way — from mistakes. A better way to choose a new company leader who would not spend the first five years learning from mistakes would be to test the fluid intelligence of every reliable and hard-working employee already working for the company and promote the person with the highest score into the position! Well, perhaps not, but the lesson should be learned that people can have achieved success despite being dull thinkers and perhaps in some cases because of it. Traditional methods usually work for someone who knows what to do, but ask the same person to do original thinking or to apply old methods to a new situation, and chaos can result.

Thus, in the workplace, the ability to learn a new job is more important than what the applicant already knows. Most employers who understand this, and who require thinking skills and judgement as employment prerequisites, have moved from measuring general and acquired knowledge — which is really a measure of memory and past experience, to IQ tests, which are a better measure of future learning ability and judgement.

Unfortunately though, fluid intelligence is not perfectly measured by psychometric IQ tests. Flexible and effective managers may not always have high IQ ratings, but they know how to deal with people, sort out problems, make fast decisions, and perhaps keep a factory in all its complexity in operation. Aptitude and personality tests may also be necessary. As another example, to obtain their taxi licence, taxi drivers in London need to have acquired 'the knowledge' — a mental map of London which enables them to go by the shortest or fastest route from A to B anywhere in the city.

Few of these taxi drivers are likely to have astonishingly high psychometric IQs, and their intelligence may not be truly fluid, but they have very high knowledge-based intelligence specific to their job. This takes a great deal of hard work and determination to acquire and gives them an advantage over other drivers in London who may have much higher psychometric intelligence. There will be also be some crossover of their skills and acquired intelligence into everyday life. Visual-spatial intelligence — which taxi drivers must necessarily acquire — is thought by many experts to be the aspect of intelligence which gives the most accurate score of natural non-culture-based intelligence. In the case of taxi drivers, this may not always hold true, but it is likely that their increased visual-spatial skills will have the effect of increasing their overall IQ score.

But like the brilliant manager or company director with knowledge-based crystallized intelligence who is recruited by another company, if the taxi driver were transported to a strange city he would be less effective for a considerable time than the locals. The taxi driver's job-specific intelligence does not have the same survival value as the previously mentioned nomad's fluid intelligence. That said, knowledge-based intelligence is highly valued by our society and is of more value to an individual who uses it than high psychometric IQ to an individual who does not use that potential. In the end, what we do with our intelligence matters more than the type or quantity of intelligence we have at our disposal.

Divergent and convergent thinking

If you have good fluid intelligence, you will be good at divergent thinking — the process of finding previously undiscovered solutions to problems, whatever the type of problem you tackle. It can take the same kind of creative intelligence to find a workable solution to a family crisis as to find a cure for a disease, or to invent a new type of engine. The tools you need to solve problems with divergent thinking are originality, adaptability, fluency, and inventiveness, and the typical divergent thinker will usually explore many possible solutions before finding the best one. It may even be true to say that only a divergent thinker can do this.

A convergent thinker is likely to pick the first viable solution that is found, and stick to that no matter what happens. Divergent thinkers have multi-track minds. Convergent thinkers have one-track minds. Henry Ford's famous (but apocyphal) slogan about the model T Ford, "You can have any color so long as it is black," is typical of a convergent thinker, but Ford was a good convergent thinker. He surrounded himself with divergent thinkers and he had a row of buzzers on his desk to summon the thinkers he needed to solve his problems. Again typical of convergent thinkers, Ford was very stubborn. Despite being told that an eight cylinder V8 engine block was technically impossible, he instructed his engineers to design and make the engine and he repeatedly refused to take no for an answer. He had picked his solution and nothing was going to change his mind. It took over a year for his design team — divergent thinkers to a man — to come up with a solution, but when they did it took the motoring world by storm. The force of combined divergent and convergent thinking working together is hard to beat.

Physical Changes

Contrary to popular belief, the brain undergoes physical changes in the process of learning. We can't make more brain cells, but we constantly make new connections between those cells in a network many thousand times more complex than the world wide telephone network. Knowledge increases that network of connections as does acquired skill and improved mental capacity of every kind. Recent studies have shown that even fluid intelligence can be improved by exercising the brain. Each cell in our brain can have up to 10,000 connections, some of which get priority over others. When we use a connection route a lot — when we learn things permanently — our brain decides to protect that connection and coats the connections with myelin, enabling faster and more reliable chemical and electrical communication. Thus, old people with Alzheimer's disease, who have forgotten everything they have learned over the past sixty years, may still be able to recall verses learned by rote in childhood, the memories protected from the ravages of Alzheimer's by myelin sheathing. Thus also, recurrent nightmares and bad memories. When something terrible happens to us, our brain ensures that we don't forget it by coating the relevant connections

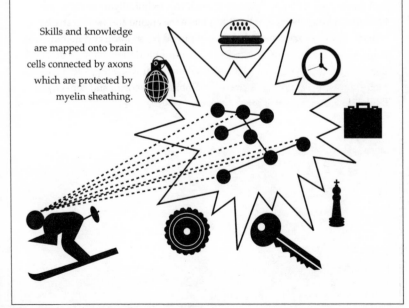

Skills and knowledge are mapped onto brain cells connected by axons which are protected by myelin sheathing.

in myelin. This is a defense mechanism to try to prevent recurrence of the harmful circumstance. But these are mapped into cerebellum; not really like cerebral memories above (in these examples, the cerebellum at the base of the brain).

This also explains why exciting lessons are easier to learn that boring ones. The brain does not invest much construction time creating new connections or protecting connections for things that apparently do not matter. Everything that happens in the brain is a matter of survival priorities. Only if something matters to us so much that we keep returning to it does the brain build protected connections to that information or skill. This is why very slow readers — like those with dyslexia, who keep having to go back over the material — when they do get through a book, know it much better than a fast reader who looked at each word only once. Because of their very short term memory for words, some dyslexic people have to learn each sentence as we would learn a poem by heart, a few words at a time. Only when they have memorized the whole sentence in this way do they make sense of it, but to do this their brain must invest in some myelin engineering. Dyslexic actors, once they have learned their lines, are most unlikely to forget them.

Learning by rote, sneered at by many, has its uses, and not just for people who are dyslexic. We can all make use of myelin engineering.

Music

Neurological scientists at the Universities of Wisconsin and California conducted a study in 78 three and four-year-olds. After recieving simple piano lessons for six months, children scored 34 percent better in IQ tests than those who had not had the lessons. This is myelin engineering in action. The children appear to have gained their IQ advantage by the exercise of translating notes on paper into music on the keyboard. This is a vital time for the creation of neural networks — the pathways of our thinking. The repetitive nature of learning music seems to give just the right kick-start to the growth and myelization of the vital axons that communicate with other parts of our brain responsible for spatial-temporal reasoning. Quite why music should have this effect, nobody yet knows, but it makes sense to take advantage of such a massive IQ boosting effect — on its own enough to more than compensate for many other disadvantages.

Genetic Components and the Bell Curve

Around 60% of our IQ potential is inherited from our parents. The remainder is affected by social and environmental factors such as living conditions, parental encouragement and mental stimulation, access to learning materials, such as in the music effect above, and nutrition. It is less likely, for example, for poor people to have access to a piano. People who lead less privileged lifestyles, wherever they live, tend to have lower average IQ levels. Animal studies have also shown that the growth of dendrites and axons in the brain — the wiring of the brain network — is dependent upon these environmental factors. Without the wiring in place our brain cells cannot communicate with each other — we cannot think. However, since our IQ can be damaged by the environment in which our brain has to operate, it follows that it can be enhanced by improving those conditions and in fact we can see this taking place. As social conditions improve throughout the developed world we see a rise in IQ levels. We may be smarter as a race and as we get smarter, it may be more likely that we raise smarter children and the cycle continues. Good so far, but a snag arises with this cycle. A healthy lifestyle in today's world is mostly achieved through wealth. We are forced to the conclusion that the wealthy will be getting smarter while the poor will not. Controversy entered this arena with the publication in 1994 of *The Bell Curve* by Herrnstein and Murray.

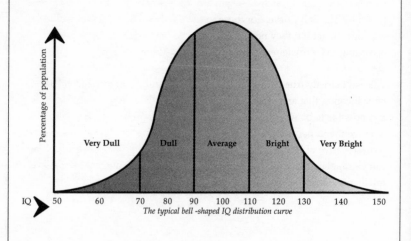

The typical bell -shaped IQ distribution curve

Based upon long term accumulation of psychometric IQ test information and upon a survey of more than 12,000 people from all social groups in the USA between the ages of 14 and 22, Herrnstein and Murray have come to the conclusion that the intelligence bipolarization is actually happening and will continue to accelerate unless we take drastic action to stop it. The book raised a storm because people do not like this conclusion. Politicians do not like it because they are, to a large extent, responsible for the living conditions of our society. The poor do not like it because it shows them to be less intelligent. Ethnic minorities do not like it because in some societies they are among the poorest and controversial claims have been made that the cause of the IQ differential is ethnic rather than wealth based. The wealthy do not like it because they would have to pay more tax to improve the living conditions of poor people.

In the end what matters is not whether people like the conclusion, but whether it is true and if so, what can be done to solve the problem. Unfortunately there is no easy solution. The poverty trap is also to some extent an IQ trap. British Mensa's recent census of members showed that the unemployment figure for Mensans is less than half the national average. Since Mensa is discrimination-free — passing a tough supervised test is the only way in — Mensans are a fairly representative sample of the top 2% of the population. This means that the less intelligent you are, the more likely you are to be unemployed — in other words, low IQ leads to poverty. Here then is the so-called Catch-22 — poverty leads to low IQ. Thus the concerns raised by The Bell Curve. For those in the poverty trap there seems no way out. To get out they need higher IQs. To have higher IQs they need, according to Herrnstein and Murray, to be wealthier.

This isn't strictly true because we know that about 8% of those in Mensa have incomes that are either close to the poverty line or below it, so just as it is possible to be wealthy and intellectually challenged, it is possible to be intelligent and poor. Thus, looking at the population as a whole, if Mensa is representative of the distribution of intelligence and poverty in society, we can extrapolate that perhaps 0.16% of the population will have Mensa level intelligence and be living in poverty.

Compare that to the 13.9% in the USA, who in 1996, according to the Economic Policy Unit, were earning at or below poverty level wages. In the UK the poverty figure is variously estimated at between 18% and 25%, but the European criteria is different, with the poverty line estimated as half of the average wage rather than at a minimum hourly income level as in the USA.

However we arrive at the figures it is clear that you are much less likely to be poor if you have an IQ in the top 2% of the population. It would be a fair assumption to say that the more intelligent you are, the less likely you are to be living in poverty. Thus, we are forced to the conclusion, like Herrnstein and Murray, that to get rid of the *poverty equals low IQ equals poverty* cycle, we need to improve society.

Unmeasurable IQ

It is not possible to measure musical aptitude or artistic talent in a standard IQ test. Neither is it possible, through an IQ test, to measure the many and various craft talents and skills — some of which require very sophisticated thinking. A carpenter, beauty consultant, printer or hairdresser needs to be able to look at any job, estimate its cost and how long it will take, work out the materials required, figure out how to do the job, and then negotiate with the person who wants the work done. The job has to be skilfully completed, working with a variety of different tools and materials, and in the majority of cases the person undertaking the work will have a greater understanding of the practicalities of the job than others with less skill but much higher measurable IQ ratings. In Scotland there is an architect who designed a roof in such a way that it could only be constructed if it were put in place before the building which was supposed to support it. The builder redesigned the roof with the comment that the architect was "All brains and no common sense."

Individual Strengths and Weaknesses

Working through this book you may discover that you have greater numerical than verbal skills, or that your ability to work with shapes — *visual-spatial intelligence* — is your greatest strength. We each have individual strengths and weaknesses. The important thing is to recognize our own abilities and apply ourselves to the things that we do best. Many talented writers claim to be hopeless with numbers, and there are mathematicians who cannot spell and surgeons who have brilliant memories and wonderful visual-spatial ability but who cannot operate a video recorder. This book will help you to recognize your strengths and weaknesses.

Look at the following problems and see which you can do most easily:
(Answers at the end of this chapter.)

Visual-Cognitive

All blocks not on the bottom row are supported by blocks underneath.

How many blocks are there?

1

Numerical

2

Continue the sequence:

$$2, \quad 3, \quad 5, \quad 10, \quad \underline{\quad}$$

Logical

3

True or false:

Some buttons are seagulls. Some chariots are seagulls. Some buttons are bananas. Some chariots are bananas. Therefore some bananas are seagulls.

Verbal-Linguistic

4

Pick the odd-word-out:

multitudinous, variegated, dappled, polychromatic, versicolored.

There are various other aspects or 'domains' to IQ, some measurable, some not. Earl Hunt, in his essay "The Role of Intelligence in Modern Society" sees intelligence as a conceptual variable and points out that the way intelligence is measured — the operational definition of that intelligence — will affect the results achieved.

Other variables involved in measuring intellect mean that it is impossible to pin an individual down to an IQ score with any degree of certainty. From day to day in comparable tests, the same person may have a measured variance of as much as thirty IQ points. Among the things that may affect your score are emotional well being (the happier you are the higher your score is likely to be within your own personal limits); circadian rhythms (sleep patterns); blood sugar levels (dependent upon the food you eat); physical fitness (studies in Manchester University have shown that the same person can score twenty points more in a comparable IQ test just by getting fit); test sophistication (the more you practice IQ tests, the better you are likely to score); and personal expectations (positive thinkers who expect to do well are likely to do better than negative thinkers who expect to fail). There are many other factors involved. Our ability to think clearly is easily affected by illness or its after-effects. It would also be foolish to take an IQ test when tired, or with Valium or marijuana or alcohol in your blood. Thus, to achieve the optimum score, it helps to do some thinking ahead.

. . . .

Answers to p. 19

1. 37.
2. 20: After the first two figures, the sequence extends by adding all the figures together.
3. False. Nothing says that the chariots and buttons which are seagulls have to overlap with those which are bananas.
4. Multitudinous. It means 'made up of lots of people', while the other words all mean 'multi–coloured'.

Motivation

A high IQ is an asset in this world, but it is only one aspect of personality, and it is often the least important aspect. Studies within Mensa and elsewhere have shown that people of high intelligence tend to be more conventionally successful than people of lower intelligence, and it has been shown that IQ and earning capacity are directly related, but not everyone who has a high IQ chooses to go down that route. You may choose not to plan your time, preferring a leisurely or disorganized existence. Success means different things to different people and to those of high intelligence and sensitivity, the quiet life can be seen as having greater value than material success. Desire for personal achievement in conventional terms has to be measured against the value of peace of mind, more unplanned free time, better family life, and perhaps, escape from the rat race. High IQ thus brings the freedom to choose in the same way that money brings freedom.

On the other hand, many people with relatively low IQ scores achieve a great deal in this world. Most people have some idea of their own limitations and will compensate for those limitations by working harder. In school and college, given an intellectually gifted student who is not motivated to work and a student with an average IQ who has a high degree of motivation, the average student will usually achieve the best results. Albert Einstein, despite having an IQ of around 169, initially failed the entrance exam for Zurich Polytechnic. Fortunately for Einstein, and for the world, he had the motivation to work at the things he enjoyed and 14 years later he became a professor at the same university.

Stories of success after failure are common among the highly intelligent. W.C. Fields, the sharp-witted comedian, lost his lifetime's savings after the age of 60. Instead of giving in to despair, he used his fluid intelligence and applied his talents to a new area — the emerging moving picture industry. He soon regained his fortune. Thomas Edison tried many thousands of combinations before he managed to get a working light bulb that was reliable. John Creasey had over 600 rejections before he got his first book published . . . If you are smart enough and persistent enough you will eventually learn what to do to achieve the success you desire.

We often find that when a person applies effort in the area which they enjoy most, they excel. But when they apply their efforts unwisely, they fail. Epicurus (300bc), put this best when he said,

> *"Every man should examine his own genius, and consider what is proper to apply himself to; for nothing can be more distant from tranquility and happiness than to be engaged in a course of life for which nature has rendered us unfit.*
>
> *An active life is not to be undertaken by an inactive person, nor an inactive life by an active person; to one, rest is quiet and action labor; to another, rest is labor and action quiet.*
>
> *A gentle man should avoid a military life, a bold and impatient man the easy; for one cannot brook war, nor the other peace."*

Test your personal motivation by completing the following quiz:

I believe this: 4 points				**C** ....
Sometimes: 2 points			**B**	
Not true: 0 points		**A**		
I am a self-made person.				
I am a good time-keeper.				
My work is very important to me.				
I plan my way ahead and follow the plan.				
I read motivational literature.				
I believe in positive thinking.				
I compete to beat others.				
I feel superior to other people.				
I make decisions quickly and stick to them.				
I keep a tidy workspace.				
Other people look up to me.				
I never get despondent.				
I keep myself fit.				
I am ambitious.				
I make my own luck.				
I complete tasks that I begin.				
I rarely procrastinate.				
I know what I want and I get it.				
I use my good ideas.				
I feel very self-assured.				
Column Totals				
Score = A+B+C				

Scoring:

80–60 points: You have very high motivation and will undoubtedly succeed.

40–58 points: You are likely to achieve material success.

20–38 points: You have some motivation, but could think more positively.

00–20 points: You are not interested in success. Relax and have a great life.

The Drawbacks of High Intelligence

High intelligence can actually be a handicap. Clever students may be bored by the lessons and spend their time daydreaming or being disruptive. Einstein's teacher of Greek once told him, "You will never amount to anything." Einstein was a teacher's worst nightmare — he asked questions which they could not answer. Although he is sometimes described as a "poor student", in fact he was top of the class in subjects which interested him. What really bored Einstein were dull uninspiring lessons, and he says, "I preferred . . . to endure all sorts of punishments rather than learn to gabble by rote."

He became so disruptive that at the age of fifteen, he was asked to leave Luitpold Gymnasium, being told that his mere presence spoiled the respect of the rest of the class for the teacher.

Faced with a child of high intelligence, parents and teachers can feel inadequate and may try to redress the balance by unconsciously bringing the child back down to a subordinate position. The cure for this problem is to be aware of it. Too many gifted children still go through school with their abilities unrecognized and may give little or no indication of their giftedness. They may even give a negative indication and have learning difficulties caused, among other things, by an inability to apply themselves to work which they find boring. It can take a lot of effort to constantly stimulate the mind of a gifted child.

High IQ children often suffer from their peers too. Nobody likes to be made to feel inferior, and children can be particularly cruel in their attempts to redress the balance. Physical and mental bullying can destroy the sensitive ego of an intellectually gifted child. With this in mind the Mensa Foundation for Gifted Children (MFGC) and other such organizations do valuable work in teacher training and in assessment, counselling and support of gifted children.

A high IQ can also be a drawback in the workplace. Employers may fear to take on anybody more intelligent than themselves in the same way that Napoleon would allow nobody taller than himself in his presence. A survey of a hundred companies recently showed that it is best not to mention membership of a high IQ society on a job application.

Intelligent people also tend to find it more difficult to fit into a comfortable place in a less intelligent society. With an IQ of 145, you are in the top three percent of the population, which means that you may have no friends or acquaintances that can talk to you on your own level. That is not quite enough to get you into Mensa, but you are likely to be the only one in your class or on the factory floor or in the office with an IQ of that level — including the teacher or the boss. That is bound to lead to a feeling of isolation. Thus, many high IQ people have learned to hide their intelligence. Students may deliberately give wrong answers in order to fit in with a class of lower intelligence. Adults may pretend to be amused by the crude jokes and prejudices of their workmates. Anything to conform.

In the words of Cecilia Francesca de Arrom, who wrote as Caballero, "Intelligence is a luxury, sometimes useless, sometimes fatal. It is a torch or firebrand according to the use one makes of it."

Fortunately the compensations of having a high IQ usually make up for the drawbacks. Intelligent people get more out of life. They have more insight into the world around us and are less likely to make the sort of mistakes which ruin lives. Hence, if they come to terms with their intelligence and find some form of intellectual release, they tend to live happier and more productive lives than their less intelligent counterparts. A 45-year study of 1000 high IQ children in California by Professor Lewis Madison Terman showed that compared to a control group they did better in every way. They earned more, had better standards of living, were less likely to turn to crime, and even had more stable relationships.

Social intelligence

Intelligence is not, of course, necessary for happiness. Even with a low psychometric IQ, If you are good at getting on with people, you are likely to be more content than someone who has a higher IQ but is no good at relationships. This is social intelligence, or SI, and it can be a very useful asset. Life is a relationship continuum and thinking skills go far beyond the ability to do puzzles. High SI individuals can often do better in life than those who have high IQ without much SI. That said, rather too much has been made of the differences and not enough of the convergences. It has to be said that it would be unusual for very high SI to exist in a person with a low IQ, and the reverse is also true. It happens, but it is not the norm. Thus, the categorizing of high IQ individuals as cold and calculating and high SI individuals as warm and caring is a false dichotomy.

It is much more difficult to measure SI than IQ. SI tests are usually of the self-analysis type such as the previous Personal Motivation Test. The results depend on the individual being truthful. Few people will willingly admit that they are cold and calculating. We are all capable of self-deceit. How many of us would fail an exam if we were responsible for marking the exam? It is not difficult to know which answer of the choices given in an SI test would be the preferred one, just as in a Rorschach ink-blot test it would be preferable for purposes of establishing your sanity to see a butterfly sitting on a wild rose rather than a vampire bat sucking your mother's blood.

Creative Intelligence

If you are more intelligent than average, there is a 50% chance that you will also be more creative than average. However, many creative people do not have high IQs and they still manage to achieve works of great merit. It is more difficult to measure creativity than to measure IQ. A standard test for creative intelligence would be to ask you, for example, to name twenty new uses for a pail of water. Do that now. You have 5 minutes (write your results in the table below):

The Bucket Test

1 ....
2 ....
3 ....
4 ....
5 ....
6 ....
7 ....
8 ....
9 ....
10 ....
11 ....
12 ....
13 ....
14 ....
15 ....
16 ....
17 ....
18 ....
19 ....
20 ....

Scoring The Bucket Test

Your thinking may be unique and highly creative, or mundane and easily thought of, and your creativity is likely to be proportional to the unique, useful and creative nature of your answers. In particular the usefulness of your answers can indicate whether your unique thought processes are the result of rational or irrational thought. Sociopaths may have unique uses for a bucket of water, but those uses are likely to involve drowning animals, committing suicide or murder, gaining revenge on those whom they feel have done them an injustice, and torture. If your answers are like that, get help!

Those who are creative but more rational are more likely to think up funny uses, or uses that could be of benefit to society as a whole, such as to pour over someone who is suffering from sunstroke, to cool the feet of those who failed at a firewalking ceremony, to use as the pendulum on a large clock, to throw over a streaker who was disrupting a game of football.

Since The Bucket Test is an open question to which you could make any reply, it would be impossible to score your answers in any definitive way here. Get someone whose judgement you trust to score the test using the following guidelines:

Score one point for every good, original and useful answer.

Half points, or no points for less good, answers, depending on originality and usefulness.

No points for sociopathic answers.

15–20 Points: You are a highly creative individual. Your creativity could make you wealthy.

10–14 Points: Very good. Your creative skills will prove useful to you.

05–09 Points: You have some good ideas. Don't let them go to waste.

00–04 Points: Creativity is not your strong point, but you probably have many other talents.

Creativity and Functional Disorders

There is some link between creativity, intelligence, mood disorders, and functional impairment. Dyslexia is unusually common among the creatively intelligent. It is as though the brain has compensated for having problems with reading and word recognition by overdeveloping some other areas, just as a blind person may develop extraordinarily acute hearing. Manic depressives too, may produce highly original and even brilliant work during their manic phase and discard it as useless during their depressive phase, only to return to the project during their next manic phase. Samuel Johnson did his writing during his manic phases. W. Axl Rose, the rock musician, produces frenzied violent music during his manic highs and gentle ballads during his lows.

One study of writers in the USA showed that 80% had mood disorders. A UK study shows that dysfunctionality is more common among all highly creative people than among those who are not creative. Creative people are more sensitive. Sensitive people are more self-analytical and are thus more likely to become unhappy with their lot. This in turn is likely to aggravate any potential for mood disorder which exists. Most psychotic episodes have trigger events such as failing an exam or being criticized by a loved one.

Other functional disorders like autism do not naturally lend themselves to divergent thinking. Autistic people are constantly looking inward, absorbed in self-centered subjective thought. They are prone to daydreaming, fantasies, hallucinations and delusions, and may find it difficult to apply themselves to exterior problems unconnected with their own well-being. However, not all autistic people are of subnormal psychometric intelligence, although even highly intelligent autists can appear to be, because of their withdrawal from the surrounding world. What most autistic people lack is the ability to put their insights to use in the world, but those who do learn to focus their very high powers of concentration can achieve the extraordinary.

Autistic savants often have much lower than normal IQ levels (between 35 and 75) and yet have very high degrees of skill, usually in one specific area — such as memory, numeracy, music, or art. The best known fictional example of this was the character Dustin Hoffman played in the film The Rain Man — a character with quite a high degree of functionality who had both an extraordinary memory and could do instant complex mental calculations. Such savants really do exist. Stephen Wiltshire is perhaps the best known of these, with his ability to produce very detailed architectural drawings from memory. Unlike artists with normal or high creative and psychometric IQ, he is able to do this even months after looking at a building.

Contrary to popular belief, we all indulge in some degree of autistic thinking and in some cases this is when we produce our best ideas. Just before falling asleep or immediately upon waking, for example, it is common for half-remembered dream images and fantasies to merge with waking thoughts, producing highly creative results. This is when eureka experiences occur, and it is often useful to keep a notepad beside the bed to jot down ideas when they occur, before they are swept away in the river of lost dreams.

Assertiveness

The people most likely to get on in this world are not always the most intelligent. It is often those who stand up and when the need arises, push to the front of the queue for the things they want. Being assertive doesn't necessarily mean trampling other people on the way to the front of the queue, but it does mean not getting trampled on yourself. On the other hand, if you are too aggressive you could be harming your career prospects just as much. Overbearing, domineering managers destroy the morale of the workforce. The best type of manager is assertive without being a bully, and sensitive to the needs of the workforce, without being a pushover.

Complete the following quiz to find out just how assertive you are, and in the process you'll discover a lot more about who you really are, and what motivates you. Be honest with yourself; self-knowledge can only come through honesty.

Assertiveness Quiz

Tick the box that most closely describes how you think you would react:

You discover that a colleague has taken credit for some of your work. Do you:

- ☐ (a) Tell your boss and insist that the colleague is reprimanded
- ☐ (b) Keep it to yourself, but never again trust the colleague
- ☐ (c) Insist that the colleague goes to your boss and explains what happened

While checking accounts you realize that you have made a serious mistake that has cost your firm money. Do you:

- ☐ (a) Arrange things so that someone else gets the blame
- ☐ (b) Hide the mistake at all costs
- ☐ (c) Admit the mistake and show how it could be avoided in future

Your boss refuses to give you time off that you need. Do you:

- ☐ (a) Threaten to quit unless you get the time off, or call in sick and take the time off anyway
- ☐ (b) Realize that you probably don't deserve the time off, and accept the decision with disappointment
- ☐ (c) Point out the value of your contribution to the firm, and offer to work extra hours to cover for the time off

You have just been awarded a large bonus for a major success at work. Do you:

4

- ☐ (a) Make sure everyone knows that it was all your own work
- ☐ (b) Get all embarrassed and try to ensure that nobody finds out
- ☐ (c) Hold a party and acknowledge that you couldn't have done it without the contribution of others

After making a major decision, you realize that it was wrong. Do you:

5

- ☐ (a) Stick to your decision, because to change your mind would show weakness
- ☐ (b) Realize that you are a fool, and that you'll never be much good at decisions, then change your mind
- ☐ (c) Reassess the situation and make another decision, in the knowledge that we all make mistakes

A friend comes to you with a problem, asking for help. Do you:

6

- ☐ (a) Tell the friend that you have your own problems to deal with, and have no time for theirs
- ☐ (b) Take the problem in hand and solve it yourself
- ☐ (c) Help if you can, without feeling obliged to

You don't understand what you are being asked to do. Do you:

7

- ☐ (a) Take your best shot, and hope to bluff your way through
- ☐ (b) Secretly ask a friend for help later
- ☐ (c) Immediately ask for more information, even if everyone else understands

Someone is cruel to you. Do you:

8

- ☐ (a) Take immediate revenge
- ☐ (b) Shrink into your shell, hurt
- ☐ (c) Confront the person, and tell them how you feel about what they did

A person whom you know to be a fool gives you a piece of advice. Do you:

9

- ☐ (a) Ignore the advice
- ☐ (b) Take the advice, because the fool probably knows better than you
- ☐ (c) Consider the advice, and take it if you find it to be sound, even if everyone else laughs

Your boss, whom you do not find attractive, makes sexual advances to you. Do you:

10
- ☐ (a) Slap him/her on the face, and storm out, before claiming constructive dismissal
- ☐ (b) Submit, in the knowledge that your job will be safeguarded
- ☐ (c) Politely reject the advance, and explain that you never mix business and pleasure

In the following questions, tick the box that most closely describes the way you feel about yourself:

About your self-image, would you say:

11
- ☐ (a) "I am better than anyone else"
- ☐ (b) "Most others are better than me"
- ☐ (c) "I am as good as anyone else"

About your decisions, would you say:

12
- ☐ (a) "I am always right"
- ☐ (b) "I am usually wrong"
- ☐ (c) "I am usually right, but I do make mistakes"

About your friends, would you say:

13
- ☐ (a) "I don't need friends"
- ☐ (b) "I don't have many friends because I'm careful whom I mix with"
- ☐ (c) "I have lots of friends and make new friends easily"

About your personal responsibility, would you say:

14
- ☐ (a) "I seek out responsibility"
- ☐ (b) "I dislike responsibility"
- ☐ (c) "I accept responsibility when I need to"

About your self-confidence, would you say:

15
- ☐ (a) "I am supremely confident"
- ☐ (b) "I lack confidence"
- ☐ (c) "I am naturally confident"

About your temper, would you say:

- ☐ (a) "I tend to fly off the handle a lot"
- ☐ (b) "I suppress my anger, but get emotionally upset"
- ☐ (c) "I express anger, but never let it get out of hand"

About your beliefs, would you say:

- ☐ (a) "I am dogmatic, because my beliefs are the right ones"
- ☐ (b) "I'm not quite sure what I believe, because I've never thought about it"
- ☐ (c) "I have come to a set of beliefs through my experience, but would be willing to change in the light of new knowledge"

About your ambitions, would you say:

- ☐ (a) "I am ruthlessly ambitious"
- ☐ (b) "I don't really have ambitions"
- ☐ (c) "I am working towards the achievement of my ambitions"

About your ability to relax, would you say:

- ☐ (a) "I rarely relax; I just don't have time"
- ☐ (b) "I can't relax; there is always something grinding on my nerves"
- ☐ (c) "I take time to relax because I feel that's important"

About your response to criticism, would you say:

- ☐ (a) "I hate being criticized, and react to it badly"
- ☐ (b) "I feel that I need criticism. I do a lot that deserves it"
- ☐ (c) "I listen to criticism and learn from it"

In the following questions, tick the box that is closest to the truth about the way you feel or react:

About stress, would you say :

- ☐ (a) "I get very stressed up by some situations."
- ☐ (b) "I just can't cope with stress, so I avoid it."
- ☐ (c) "I cope well with stress. I use it to keep me on top."

About doing things:

- ☐ (a) "Just to be awkward, I refuse to do things that people want me to do."
- ☐ (b) "I just can't seem to say no when others want me to do things."
- ☐ (c) "If I don't want to do something, I politely refuse to do it, because my wants are important."

About arguments:
- [ ] (a) "I never lose an argument, because I don't give in."
- [ ] (b) "I can't argue with people. It is a waste of time even trying, because I always lose."
- [ ] (c) "I state my case, but when someone can't see my point of view I don't argue after letting them know what I feel."

About trust:
- [ ] (a) "I don't trust others, and they don't trust me."
- [ ] (b) "I'd like other people to trust me, but rarely seem to get that trust. I tend to give my trust to those who break it."
- [ ] (c) "I enjoy the trust of others, and those I give my trust to rarely break it."

About flattery:
- [ ] (a) "I like to have people around who will flatter me."
- [ ] (b) "I suspect that when people flatter me, they are being dishonest."
- [ ] (c) "I can accept honest flattery, because I have worth, but I discourage crawlers."

About team-sports:
- [ ] (a) "I enjoy team-sports, but I get angry when other players can't keep up with me, or when they make mistakes."
- [ ] (b) "I dislike team-sports, and I'm not very good at them."
- [ ] (c) "I enjoy team-sports, and I'm good at them."

At meetings:
- [ ] (a) "I make sure that everyone hears what I have to say, whether they want to or not."
- [ ] (b) "I'm nervous about speaking out in front of others, so I tend to hide in a corner."
- [ ] (c) "I speak up when I have a valid point to make."

About approval:
- [ ] (a) "I neither want nor need the approval of others."
- [ ] (b) "I have a need for the approval of others."
- [ ] (c) "I don't need the approval of others for what I do, but when I get it I'm happy."

About truth:

29

- ☐ (a) "I tell people what I think even if it hurts them."
- ☐ (b) "I tell lies to avoid unpleasant situations."
- ☐ (c) "I generally speak the truth, but I'll tell a lie to avoid hurting others."

About physical control:

30

- ☐ (a) "I've been known to lash out in anger, but I'm always sorry afterwards."
- ☐ (b) "I've never had the urge to lash out."
- ☐ (c) "I've sometimes felt like lashing out, but I always restrain myself."

Scoring the Assertiveness Quiz

The greatest value in this type of quiz is what you learn about yourself in the process of completing it. The following comments are for guidance, but where they stray from what you feel to be true, go with your instincts. If you score close to a borderline, read the next comments too.

Score mostly Cs:

You are assertive, but not to the point of being overbearing. You are cool, controlled and confident, with just the right amount of consideration for others. You have a very high degree of social intelligence. You are fully aware of your right to have and assert your own needs, and to express your feelings, and with your excellent judgement of human nature you can see when others lack your qualities. You are helpful to others, but if you don't want to do something you know that you have the right to refuse, and you don't get embarrassed at saying no. Because you know how to be diplomatic you usually get what you want. With your high intelligence, your confidence in your own abilities, and your top people-management skills you deserve to be in a good management position. Don't let your talents go to waste.

Score mostly Bs:

You have many wonderful qualities, such as kindness, compassion, and sensitivity, but you are too considerate for your own good. You are trying too hard to fit in. People are bound to take advantage of you if you behave like a human door-mat. You are also a timebomb of suppressed emotions. You may get tension headaches and other psychosomatic problems. Your career is unlikely to be progressing much — if you get promoted it will be because someone has died or left. To change things you need to become more assertive. Learn to say what you think. Don't be afraid to express your emotions, and don't be so afraid of what others think. You don't have to give up caring for others to have your own wants and needs fulfilled. Your place in this world is just as important as anyone else's.

Score mostly As:

You are assertive to the point of being a bully. This doesn't mean that you are necessarily a bad person, but you have got into a system of thinking, and a pattern of life that is non-beneficial. You are likely to have very high psychometric IQ, but by your aggressiveness you alienate people, and instead of getting more co-operation out of them you get less. You probably lack genuine confidence, and cover that up with bluster and brashness. You will have few if any genuine friends, although you may, if you are in a senior position at work have a number of `hangers on' who pretend to like you because they are scared of you. Your social life is likely to be non-existent, unless you go out on your own, and you may be very unhappy with your present life.

The way to change is to start recognizing the rights of others. What you need is important, but what other people need is important too. To have a friend you need to be a friend. Everyone has the right to be treated with respect, and even if you are superior to them in rank or position, you have no right to bully them. Gradually, you will find that when you give people respect, and take their wants and needs into account, you will receive respect and generosity in return, and your currently low self-esteem will be replaced by a new feeling of personal worth.

Male-female differences

On average, men have brains which are slightly larger than the brains of women, but the difference is because men, on the whole, are bigger than women. There is no overall IQ differential between men and women. Men are better at spatial and related problems; women are better at verbal-linguistic problems. Interestingly there is a large hormonal component to the differential. During menstruation, when women have low estrogen levels, their spatial cognitive powers can double. They are also more likely to be assertive at this time. Men do best at verbal problems when their testosterone levels are lowest, but are less likely to be assertive at this time. Girls who have been subjected to high levels of testosterone in the womb develop unusually high visual-spatial abilities and other masculine traits.

There are other forces at work here too. Although girls tend to apply themselves more to schoolwork, research has shown that girls taught in an all-girl class do better in related subjects such as science, technical drawing, and maths, than they would if taught in a mixed class. When there are boys present the boys tend to be more pushy than girls and thus attract more of the teacher's time. Thus, although girls are working harder and should do better, they are receiving less teaching time and so do worse. Teachers can do a lot to help balance the books in this area by ensuring that they divide their time equally.

Artificial intelligence

Computers are currently doubling in power every eighteen months and we now have computers which can recognize voices and respond to commands. They have "learned" to react to light and darkness, recognize shapes, communicate with us and with each other, and in some cases, self-repair.

Computers can even write poetry, and recently the first novel by a computer has been published, but this does not mean that computers can think. Not yet anyway. The poetry is not very good, and the novel was not very literate.

Probably the area where computers have the greatest `thinking' success is in chess, but even here we are at a very early stage of development. It took a great deal of human input for IBM's Deep Blue computer to beat World Chess Champion Gary Kasparov. And in the sense of humor department, not normally Kasparov's greatest strength, he beat the computer hands down.

Long before Kasparov's encounter with Deep Blue, the British computer scientist Alan Turing looked at the question of whether machines can think and proposed a test of computer IQ which has now been dubbed the Turing test. Turing's test was simple — If you can be fooled by the computer into thinking it is a person — by communicating through a phone or a keyboard the computer can be said to think. So far, no computer has ever passed the Turing test when faced with the penetrating questions of an inquisitive human. When a sentence structure that the computer is incapable of answering comes along, computers are programmed to respond by incorporating that word structure or meaning into the answer. For example, if you were to ask the computer, "Tell me why it is better to fall in love than to eat a shrimp," the computer may answer, "Why do you ask me such a foolish question about love and shrimps?"

A human respondent, on the other hand, would be more likely to say, "Love is food for the soul, but a shrimp is food only for the body."

How long will it be before a computer can compare with the wit of Voltaire, who, when told that life is hard, asked, "Compared to what?"

Initially a correspondent may be fooled by the computer's answer, but a number of abstract questions or statements are likely to reveal the computer's lack of thinking depth to a respondent with good human IQ. That said, less intelligent respondents are more likely to be fooled by the computer, and with greater computer power and more complex algorithms, the time will come when the average desktop computer will be able to pass the Turing test with ease.

Critical Thinking

In this modern age we are exposed to a great deal of information from many sources and it is not always easy to judge the accuracy of the information that comes our way. The following nine steps form a good framework for judgement of the accuracy of any argument. Ask yourself the following:

1. What are the problems addressed and the conclusions reached?

2. What is the justification for reaching these conclusions?

3. Are the originator's conclusions logical and valid?

4. What errors in reasoning have been made by the originator?

5. Which words or phrases are ambiguous?

6. Have assumptions have been made, and if so, are they based on logic?

7. Has the originator used relevant analogies or metaphors?

8. Could entirely different conclusions have been consistent with the facts?

9. Are there rival hypotheses to those which the originator uses?

A good IQ does not necessarily make you a clear thinker, it merely indicates that you have the potential to be so. Many mistakes are possible, even for the intellectually gifted. Some of the mistakes are obvious, others less so. Thinking accurately is a skill that needs to be learned like any other skill

To quote Shakespeare,

"Thoughts are but dreams till their effects be tried."

Here are some of the most common errors of thinking and their cures:

Error	Details or Example	Workaround
Using a non sequitur	Reasoning that does not follow logically from anything previously said	Critically examine all conclusions to see if they are logical
Plunging in	Gathering information and reaching conclusions too soon	Ensure that you know what the real problem is that you have to solve
Jumping to conclusions	Guessing the answer to a problem rather than solving the problem	Collect key factual information and use that to solve problems
Failure to distinguish between fact and opinion	Believing rumor to be true. Relying on anecdotal evidence	Check the truth of statements before believing them
Lack of problem definition	Failing to consciously define the problem or being unduly influenced by the definitions of others	Examine what is actually happening. Define problems from your own evidence
Not using the all facts	Lack of research or selection of facts which fit your preconceptions.	Find out all the facts and base your decisions upon them
Prejudice	The inclination to take a stand with insufficient information	Never prejudge people or situations. Do not defend or attack without good reason
Self-deceit	Failing to understand your own limitations. Believing that you are more able than you are	Acquiring self-knowledge
Lack of discrimination	Failing to weigh the facts according to importance. Believing that all propositions are equally valid	Careful consideration of what matters and what does not matter
Filling a personal need	Embracing arguments that meet your personal requirements	Detach yourself from the argument.
Over-simplification	Ignoring the middle ground in a controversy	Embrace complexity and organize and consider all the facts
False syllogism	All ducks have feathers. All birds have feathers. Therefore all birds are ducks	Because D has f and B has f does not make B = D. Other things may also have f
Circular argument	I know that this book is true because this is a book which is known to be true	Seek empirical evidence of the truth
Closed thinking	What is the point of investigating this when I already know the truth?	Keep an open mind. You may hold wrong opinions

Organized Thinking

Few people have a clear idea of what they want from life. It is ironic that we are likely to spend more time planning our annual vacation than planning our lives. We tend to let life happen and when it does it takes us by surprise. Planning is one of those things we approve of, but rarely indulge in, but it is fundamental to the process of problem solving. Whatever your problem, you have to plan how to solve it, and most situations in life can be viewed as problems to be solved. If you want to pass an exam, the problem is *how can I ensure that I pass this exam?* . . . . Those who plan study periods into their schedule achieve more success in exams. If you want a successful career, the problem is *how can I have a successful career?* . . . . Those who plan their career achieve more promotion and job success.

It all boils down to planning our time. Those who plan their time achieve more of everything.

> *"There is nothing of which we are apt to be so lavish as of time, and about which we ought to be more solicitous; since without it we can do nothing in this world. Time is what we want most, but alas! we use worst. . ."*

William Penn

William Penn's famous book *Some Fruits of Solitude*, was written, like a number of his works, while he was in prison for expressing his political and religious beliefs. Like Voltaire, who started *Henriade* in prison — the poem that made him famous, and Aleksandr Solzhenitsyn, who wrote and memorized *One Day in the Life of Ivan Denisovitch* while in a labor camp, and John Bunyan, who began *Pilgrim's Progress* in prison, Penn made good use of his time in prison rather than waste it. Better use, no doubt, than most who were free. Thus he became an inspiring leader to many.

Deep down, despite the tendency to deceive ourselves, we all know that we waste too much time. No matter what our IQ, we all procrastinate. We let our dreams trickle down the TV tube. We never get round to taking that cruise, or learning that language, or building that boat. Our best days slip away like shadows, while we idly watch them pass.

Asked to instantly choose between 2,700; 27,000; 270,000; and 27,000,000 as the number of days in the average life, (choose now!) most people are overoptimistic by at least a factor of 10. In fact, based on a lifetime of 73 years, we have less than 27,000 days to live. It doesn't seem much because it is not much. We may, of course, have more, but we may have much less, and a lot of us will already be more than halfway there. The truth is that we have no way of knowing what the future holds. We can rely only on the time we have right now.

Isaac Pitman, inventor of the shorthand system of writing, said, "Well-arranged time is the surest mark of a well-arranged mind," and that seems to be true in every case, just as the converse is true. In fact, since we think sequentially, our thoughts are organized in time sequence, so by organizing our time we organize the way we think, and this in turn can improve our creativity and boost our performance in every area, affecting both our psychometric IQ score and our ability to make use of that intelligence in the real world.

In business especially, using our time to the fullest can pay great dividends. Since most people waste hours of every working day, those who really make use of their time can achieve more — sometimes so much more that others are astonished. That is why, if you want something done, it is usually better to ask a busy person. However, there are many ways of being busy. Disorganized people can be twice as busy achieving nothing as organized people are getting things done. In the words of Benjamin Franklin, "He who does everything, does nothing."

17 Steps to Organized Thinking

1. Plan each day the night before.

Write the things you need to do on separate cards and stack them in order of priority. The following day, start with the top card and tackle them one at a time until they have all been completed. Keep a few blank cards for the unexpected. (Ordinary business cards are great for the purpose and are very inexpensive when blank. Plus, they are easy to slip into your purse or pocket.)

2. Use the do-it-now system.

Don't keep a pending tray, either mentally, or actually. Deal with paper the first time it is read. This is the most valuable of all time-savers, and since the only way the do-it-now system can be implemented is to become an instant decision maker, it can transform your life on the spot. But it means no more put-off letters and phone calls.

3. Speed-read.

The simple action of trying to read faster can double the average reading speed. Get into the SEE mode - Scan for Essential Elements. Practice the IJMBT - Instant Junk Mail Bin Trick.

4. Always do what you say you will do.

If you don't, your valuable time will be wasted by people chasing you up to find out why things haven't been done. Putting them off just wastes more time, because they'll get back to you again and again. Don't make promises unless you intend to keep them. Don't fail to keep them when you do make them.

5. Be concise.

Write memos instead of letters. Most letters can boil down to two words:
Well done; Try harder; Good luck; Hard luck; Thank you; See me.

6. Delegate willingly.

Don't believe that you're the only one that can do a task. If that were true,
promotion would be impossible. Delegation also helps to make other people
feel important and to upgrade their skills. It is also good planning. The more
you delegate, the more you'll be able to delegate in future, and the more time
you'll have free.

7. Stay focussed.

Loss of mental focus accounts for almost a third of the time taken for tasks.
With focussed attention therefore, a third as much again can be achieved
each day. Repeat the words `stay focussed' whenever you feel a lapse coming
on. It'll soon become a habit that saves you hours.

8. Solve problems immediately.

They will arise, so don't let them accumulate. It also makes sense not to
cause them in the first place. Never argue. Arguing is time-wasting. If you
have the power, make decisions and stick to them. If you don't have that
power, compromise with good grace as soon as you can.

9. Cancel unnecessary meetings.

That means most meetings. Remember that people make more effective
decisions when they are alone, and that includes you. If you do have to
attend meetings, keep them as short as possible. People use meetings as
excuses not to get work done.

10. Limit time on phone calls.

Before you make calls, jot down the subjects you have to deal with. On the phone go through them as fast as possible, then make excuses and hang up. If you are expecting a call from someone else, again have a list of topics pre-prepared. This is a useful technique even on personal calls.

11. Set tight deadlines for yourself and others.

Deadlines force people to perform at peak. When you set the deadlines, listen carefully to the response. 'Perhaps,' usually means 'No,' and, 'I'll try,' usually means 'I won't.' Extract certainty from those you deal with instead of uncertainty. Then, you'll be able to mark the deadline in your calendar and plan ahead.

12. Keep a tidy desk.

A cluttered workspace wastes time. You can't be efficient if you spend half your time chasing lost paper. Worse still, if you keep a cluttered desk and you are the boss, other people will emulate your inefficiency, with a resultant effect on your business. If necessary go in at the weekend to clear the desk. With the do-it-now system, if something doesn't go into the out tray, it goes into the wastepaper basket. But don't ever throw out something you haven't yet dealt with. It'll come back to haunt you.

13. Plan ahead.

If you try to run a business, or even a holiday without planning, it is like trying to cook a meal without ingredients. Diary spaces mean wasted time unless you know in advance what you'll be doing during those times. Plan to use the free periods profitably.

14. Concentrate on the small things.

Save five minutes here, five minutes there, and it all adds up. Get up five minutes earlier. Spend five minutes less in the toilet. Take five minutes less coffee-break. Time yourself on the things you need to get done and do them faster each time.

15. Don't say yes when you mean no.

If you take more work than you can handle, you'll regret it later and have to deal with the problems it causes you.

16. Never make the same mistake twice.

Nothing wastes time like mistakes. We profit from them the first time they happen, because we learn. But the next time they happen, we lose time, energy, and profit.

17. Don't ever take work home.

To do so is an admission of inefficiency at work. Tackle the inefficiency instead. The freed 'home-work' time can be used for far more important things. What, after all, is the point in saving time if we are so busy running around saving it that there is no time left for the good things in life?

With just a little bit of thought, it is possible to also greatly improve our personal lives by organizing time — surely an equally good way to use our intellect. We can plan breakfast in bed, or romantic evenings. We can plan quality time with the children, or weekends away that would be impossible without thinking ahead. Each important minute, of each and every day, we have the ultimate choice that makes anything and everything possible: what to do next. Choose wisely. Then, no matter what your IQ, it is possible to achieve a great deal.

Find the starting point and move from square to adjoining square, horizontally or vertically, but not diagonally, to spell a 12-letter word, using each letter once only. What are the missing letters?

E		I
R	B	A
A		T
	O	I

Find two words with different spellings, but which sound alike, that can mean:

FROLIC / CHANCE

What number should replace the question mark?

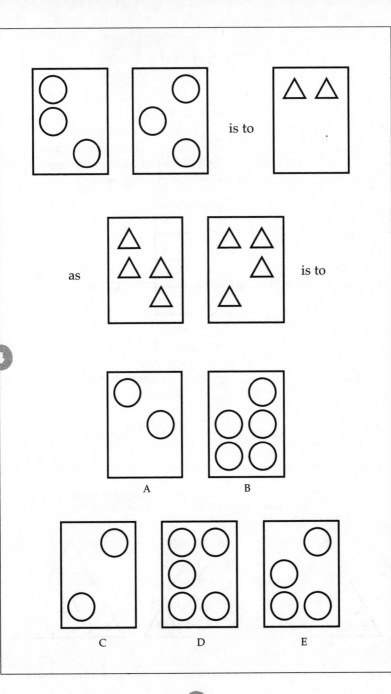

is to

as

is to

A   B

C   D   E

482 : 34

Which two numbers below have the same relationship
as the two above?

A. 218 : 24
B. 946 : 42
C. 687 : 62
D. 299 : 26
E. 749 : 67

GIBE is to TAUNT as BADINAGE is to:

A. PRANK
B. REPARTEE
C. PLEASANTRY
D. WITTICISM
E. JOKE

Which of the following is the odd one out?

A. CUBE
B. SQUARE
C. SPHERE
D. CYLINDER
E. OCTAHEDRON

8 If you divide 552 by ¼, and then divide the result by half the original figure, what is the answer?

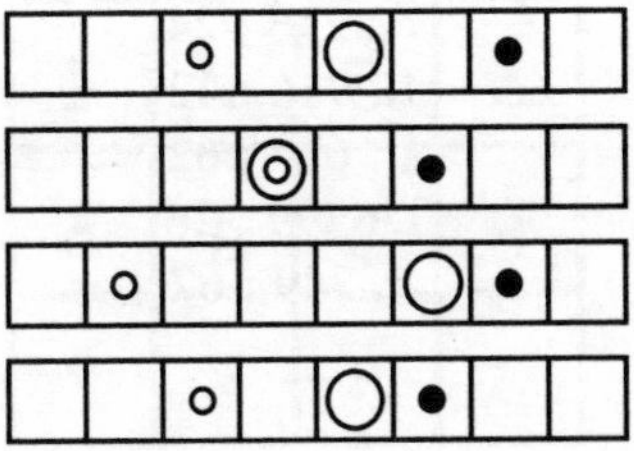

9 What figure below will continue the above sequence?

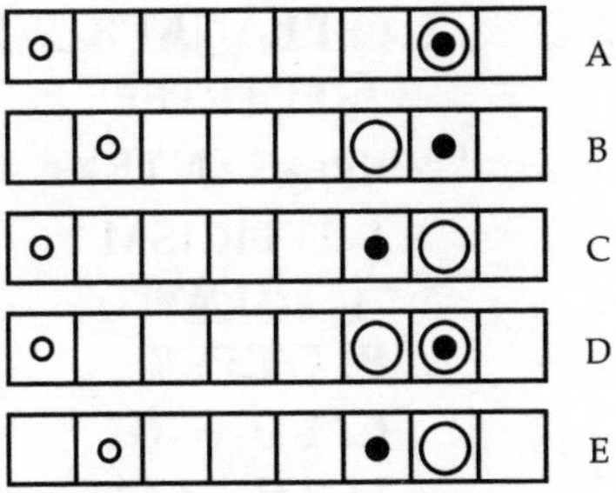

A
B
C
D
E

What word is opposite in meaning to EVASIVE?

A. ZEALOUS
B. EXACT
C. OPEN
D. CAUSTIC
E. BRAVE

10

What number should replace the question mark below?

6	3	4	6
5	5	7	4
8	3	4	8
3	9	7	?

11

PLEAD   LABEL   ALBUM   LUSTY?

What word continues the above sequence?

12

        A. FROWN
        B. UTTER
        C. LUNCH
        D. DREAM
        E. CHARM

What is the answer if, from the number below, you multiply by five the number of even numbers that are immediately followed by an odd number?

13

4 7 8 5 3 1 9 7 8 4 4 7 8 9 2 3

Which of the five boxes below is most like the box above?

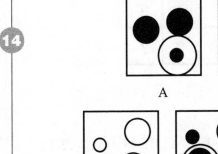

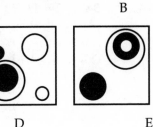

A   B

C   D   E

SEA PIGEON is an anagram of what nine-letter word?

Which of the following is the odd one out?

A. SKIT
B. EMERITUS
C. LAMPOON
D. CLERIHEW
E. PARODY

Find a six-letter word made up of only the
following four letters.

G M
N O

What number should replace the question mark?

34 7 29 11 23 16 16 22 ?

A. 3
B. 5
C. 8
D. 11
E. 13

What word can be placed in front of the other five to form
five new words? Each dot represents a letter.

(• • • •) ⟨ PING
            DRAGON
            SHOT
            BRIM
            PER

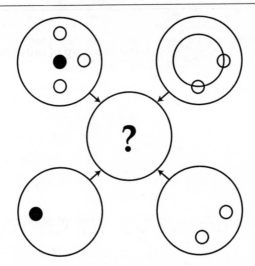

Each line and symbol that appears in the four outer circles, above, is transferred to the middle circle according to how many times it appears, as follows:

One time — it is transferred
Two times — it is possibly transferred
Three times — it is transferred
Four times — it is not transferred

Which of the circles below should appear as the middle circle?

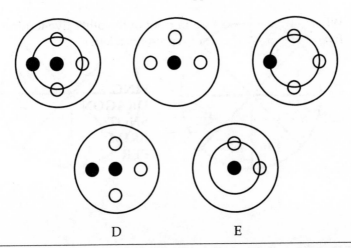

D   E

A word can be placed in the brackets that has the same meaning as the words outside. What is it?

ENCLOSURE (• • • • • • • •) COMBINATION

Place two of the three-letter segments together to make a six-letter bug.

ANT BEE SCA TLY RAB FLY

If the missing letters in the two circles below are correctly inserted they will form synonymous words. The words do not necessarily have to be read in a clockwise direction, but the letters are in order. What are the words and missing letters?

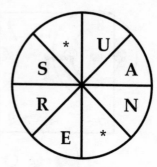

58

24

What number should replace the question mark?

A. 30
B. 32
C. 34
D. 36
E. 38

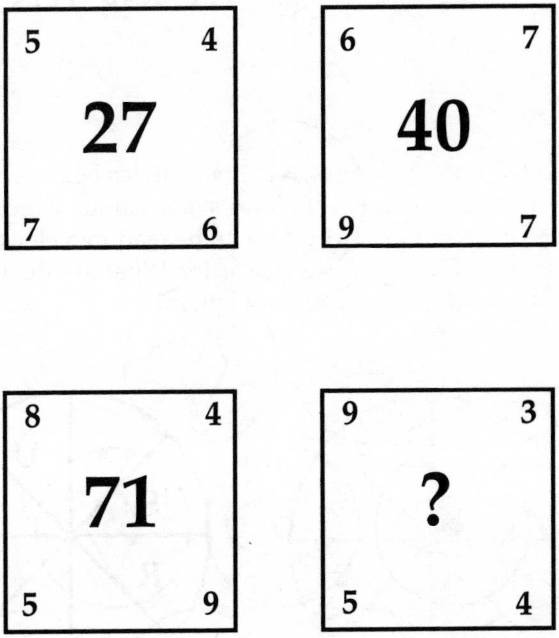

What circle will continue the sequence and
replace the question mark?

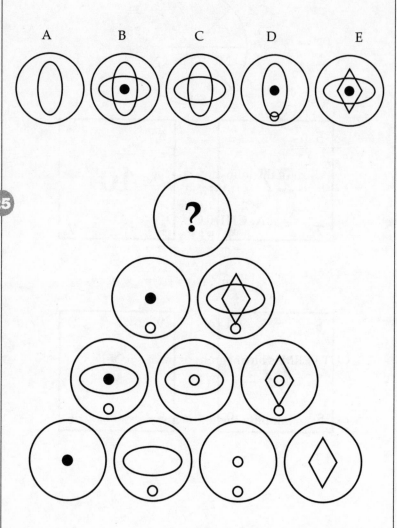

If the missing letters in the circle below are correctly inserted they will form an eight-letter word. The word will not necessarily have to be read in a clockwise direction, but the letters are in order. What is the word and missing letters?

Which of the following has the same meaning as MENDICANT?

A. CHURCH OFFICIAL
B. REPAIRER
C. TEACHER
D. BEGGAR
E. CHEMIST

CUT PERM is an anagram of what seven-letter word?

Simplify the following and find x.

$$\frac{8 \times 7}{{}^2\!/_7 - {}^2\!/_{14}} = x$$

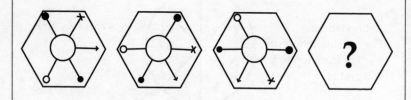

Which of A, B, C, D, or E, bottom should replace the
question mark above?

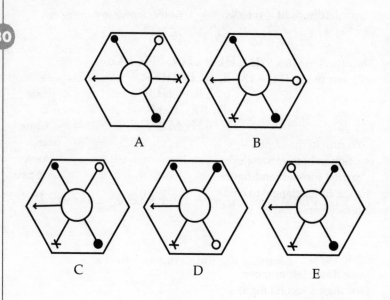

Answers

Test One

1 Abbreviation.
The missing letters are, reading from top to bottom, V, B and N.

2 Gambol and gamble.

3 15.
(Top x left) + right = middle.
(7 x 8) [56] + 15 = 71.

The others are (6 x 9) [54] + 19 = 73 and (9 x 6) [54] + 13 = 67.

4 E.
No figure in the same position in both rectangles is carried forward and figures change from triangle to circle and vice versa.

5 B (946 : 42).
Break down left number: (First digit x second digit) + third digit = right number.
(9 x 4) [36] + 6 = 42.
The example was (4 x 8) [32] + 2 = 34.

6 B (Repartee).
Repartee is a synonym for badinage, as taunt is for gibe.

7 B (Square).
The others are three-dimensional; a square is two-dimensional.

8 8.
$552 ÷ \frac{1}{4} = 2208$; $2208 ÷ 276$ (half of 552) = 8.

9 A.
There are three sequences, all alternate: the small white circle moves one forward and two back; the large white circle moves one back and two forward; the small black circle moves one back and two forward.

10 C (Open).

11 6.
Reading down, the sum of numbers on each row increases by two.

12 Utter.
Each word starts with the second letter of the previous one.

13 25.
There are five odd numbers which follow an even one, so 5 x 5 = 25.

14 E.
There are four circles, two black (medium-sized) and two white (one large, one small).

15 Espionage.

16 B. Emeritus.
The others are terms for lightly poking fun.

17 Gnomon (a pointer on a sundial).

18 C (8).
Alternate numbers go in different sequence:
− 5, − 6, − 7, and − 8; + 4, + 5, + 6.

19 Snap.

20 A.

21 Compound.

22 Scarab.

23 Misspend, squander. The missing letters are M and P (misspend), Q and R (squander).

24 C (34).
The sums are (top left x bottom right) – (bottom left – top right) = middle.
(9 x 4) [36] – (5 – 3) [2] = 34.

The others are
(5 x 6) [30] – (7 – 4) [3] = 27;
(6 x 7) [42] – (9 – 7) [2] = 40;
(8 x 9) [72] – (5 – 4) [1] = 71.

25 E.
Different symbols in adjoining circles on the same row are carried into the circle between them in the row above.
Similar symbols in the same place are dropped.

64

Henchman.

26 The missing letters are both H.

27 D (beggar).

28 Crumpet.

392.

29 $^2/_{14} = ^1/_7$, so $^2/_7 - ^1/_7 = ^1/_7$.
$8 \times 7 = 56$. $56 \div ^1/_7 = 56 \times ^7/_1$.
$56 \times 7 = 392$.

C.

30 Every item rotates 60° clockwise each time.

Test **Two**

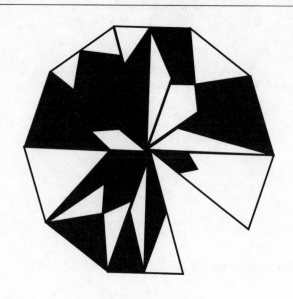

1

Which of the segments below is missing from the diagram above?

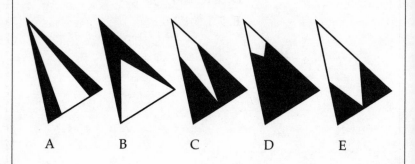

A   B   C   D   E

Complete the three-letter words which, reading down,
will reveal a country.

T	E	(•)
N	I	(•)
F	O	(•)
T	I	(•)
B	A	(•)
K	O	(•)
E	R	(•)

---

2 1 7 3 8 9 5 is to 9 7 2 5 3 8 1 as 9 6 7 4 8 1 2 is to:

A. 7 1 9 2 4 8 6
B. 7 9 1 4 2 6 8
C. 2 1 4 7 9 6 8
D. 1 7 9 2 4 8 6
E. 7 1 9 4 2 6 8

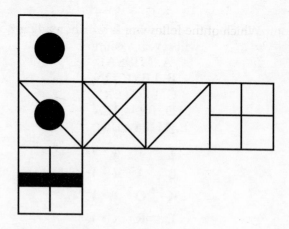

3

When the above is folded to form a cube, just one of the following can be produced. Which one is it?

4

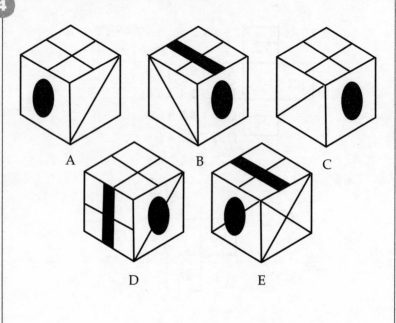

A   B   C

D   E

Which of the following is the odd one out?

A. MISSAL
B. LEXICON
C. LECTERN
D. PSALTER
E. THESAURUS

What number will replace the question mark?

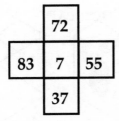

	72				19	
83	7	55		25	3	13
	37				4	

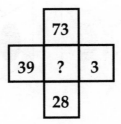

	73	
39	?	3
	28	

Which word is a synonym of EXPRESSIVE?

A. PARTICULAR
B. MEANINGFUL
C. POSITIVE
D. INSCRUTABLE
E. ELEGANT

7

Complete the two words using all the letters of the following phrase once only.

CASE A DOOR PAD

• E • • R • T • •   • E • • R • T • •

8

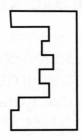

Which piece, below, can be put with the one above
to form a perfect square?

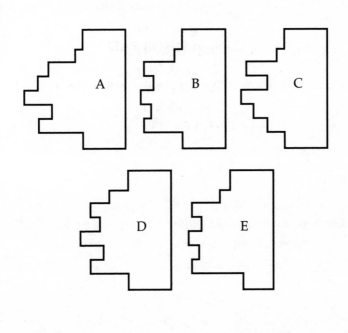

SECOND (ARDENT) NATURE

10

Following the same rules as the words above,
what word should go in the brackets?

VALISE (• • • • • •) OPENLY

What two words are opposite in meaning?

11

A. EXPAND
B. DELIGHT
C. UPSURGE
D. OFFEND
E. UPEND
F. EQUATE

Ken is half again as old as Phil, who is half again as old
as David. Their ages total 152. How old is Phil?

12

DOUBT : CONVICTION

Which two words below have the same relationship as the two words above?

A. faultless : exemplary

B. fastidious : slender

C. courage : resolution

D. instinct : constancy

E. routine : abnormal

Which of the following is the odd one out?

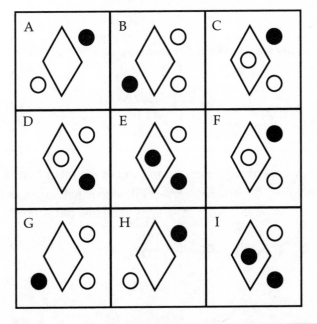

Which of the following is not an anagram of a fruit?

A. MINK PUP
B. BURY REBEL
C. USA MAST
D. MANS GUT
E. DAMN RAIN

15

What number should replace the question mark?

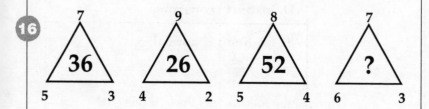

16

Find a six-letter word made up of only the following
four letters?

L O
G I

17

What word can be placed in front of the other five to form
five new words? Each dot represents a letter.

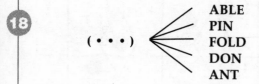

18

ABLE
PIN
FOLD
DON
ANT

DEAD LIVER is an anagram of what nine-letter word?

Each of the nine squares in the grid marked 1A to 3C should incorporate all of the items which are shown in the squares of the same letter and number, at the left and top, respectively. For example, 2B should incorporate all of the symbols that are in squares 2 and B. One square, however, is incorrect. Which one is it?

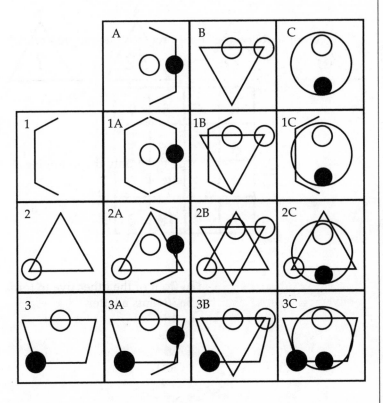

What word is a synonym of PAROXYSM?

A. SEIZURE
B. SUPERABUNDANCE
C. SPASMODIC
D. SPACE
E. PARODY

Which of the following should replace the question mark?

6	2	5	7
8	3	17	7
9	2	9	9
7	4	10	?

A. 24
B. 30
C. 18
D. 12
E. 26

If the missing letters in the circle below are correctly inserted they will form an eight-letter word. The word will not necessarily have to be read in a clockwise direction, but the letters are in order. What is the word and missing letters?

A word can be placed in the brackets that has the same meaning as the words outside. What is it?

RUMMAGE (• • • • • •) POLECAT

Which of the following is the odd one out?

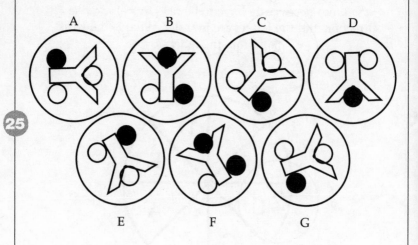

Place two three-letter segments together to form a shade

ISE   SCA   YEL   LEW   CER   LET

What number should replace the question mark?

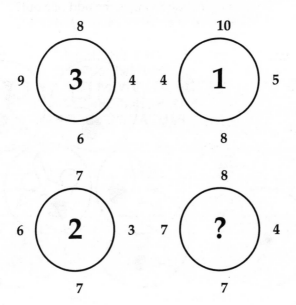

If the missing letters in the two circles below are correctly inserted they will form synonymous words. The words do not necessarily have to be read in a clockwise direction, but the letters are in order. What are the words and missing letters?

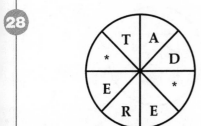

What word is an antonym of LAMBENT?

A. FLICKERING
B. TWINKLING
C. GLOWING
D. SLUGGISH
E. HEAVINESS

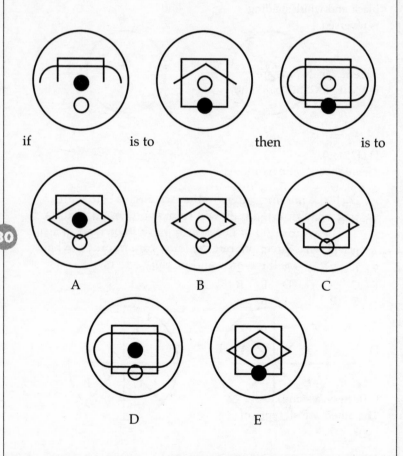

if   is to   then   is to

A   B   C

D   E

Answers

Test Two

E.
Opposite segments are mirror images except that black and white shading is reversed.

Algeria. The words are: teA, niL, foG, tiE, baR, koI, and erA.

D (179486).
The numbers were reordered as follows: sixth, third, first, seventh, fourth, fifth, second. Therefore the new order is:

A	B	C	D	E	F	G
9	6	7	4	8	1	2
F	C	A	G	D	E	B
1	7	9	2	4	8	6

D.

C (lectern, a stand).
The others are all types of book.

9.
(Top+Right)–(Bottom+Left) = Middle.
(73+3)–(39+28) = 76–67 = 9
Others are:
(72+55)–(83+37) = 127–120 = 7
and
(19+13)–(25+4) = 32–29 = 3

Meaningful.

Separated and decorator.

B.

10. Please. Three specific letters of both left and right words transfer to the middle as follows:

V	A	L	I	S	E
	4			5	3

(P	L	E	A	S	E)
1	2	3	4	5	6

O	P	E	N	L	Y
	1	6		2	

81

11 Delight, offend.

12 Phil is 48 years old. Ken is 72 and David is 32.

13 E (routine : abnormal). They are antonyms as are doubt and conviction.

14 D.
The others all have identical pairs: A and H, B and G, C and F, and E and I.

15 MANS GUT (mustang). The others are pumpkin (milk pup), blueberry (bury rebel), satsuma (USA mast) and mandarin (damn rain).

16 39.
The sums are (top + left) x right = middle.
(7 + 6) [13] x 3 = 39.
Others are:
(7 + 5) [12] x 3 = 36;
(9 + 4) [13] x 2 = 26;
(8 + 5) [13] x 4 = 52.

17 Gigolo, googol (a huge number, 10^{100}), or loligo (a type of squid).

18 Ten.

19 Daredevil.

20 3A (missing central circle).

21 A (seizure).

22 C (18).
Reading from the left along each row, (first column x second column) – third column = fourth column.
(7 x 4) [28] – 10 = 18.
Others are:
(6 x 2) [12] – 5 = 7;
(8 x 3) [24] – 17 = 7;
(9 x 2) [18] – 9 = 9.

23 Sluggard. The missing letters are S and G.

24 Ferret.

25 D.
The others all have identical pairs: A and E, B and F, and C and G.

26 Cerise.

2.
The sums are (top x left) ÷
(right x bottom) = middle.
(8 x 7) [56] ÷ (7 x 4) [28] = 2.

27 The others are
(8 x 9) [72] ÷ (4 x 6) [24] = 3;
(10 x 4) [40] ÷ (5 x 8) [40] = 1;
(7 x 6) [42] x (3 x 7) [21] = 2.

Adherent, believer. The
28 missing letters are H and
N (adherent) and B and E
(believer).

29 C (glowing).

A. The black and white dots
change position; the full
square becomes a half-square
30 and vice versa; and the oval
becomes a diamond and vice
versa (remaining a half-shape
where appropriate).

Which of the following is the odd one out?

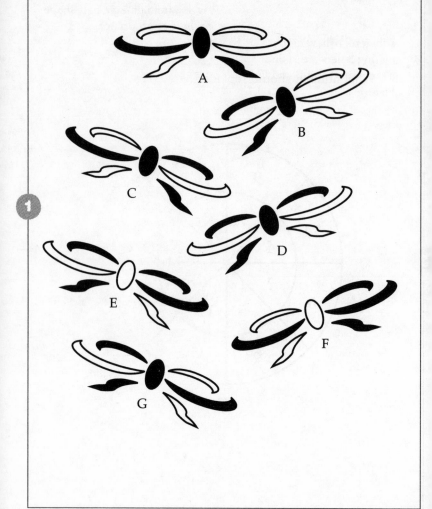

GLOSSY METALS is an anagram of which well-known three-word phrase (3, 7, 2) which could also be "ready for the off."

- - - - - - - - - -

What number should replace the question mark?

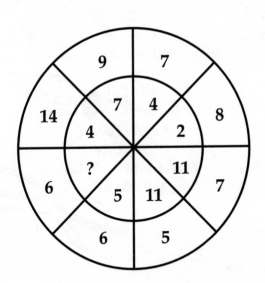

Start at a corner square and move in a clockwise spiral to the middle to spell out a nine-letter word. What are the missing letters?

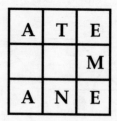

4

A	T	E
		M
A	N	E

What words are antonymous?

5

A. ABSTRUSE
B. DEFICIENT
C. PROFLIGATE
D. SECURE
E. PARSIMONIOUS
F. EXOTIC

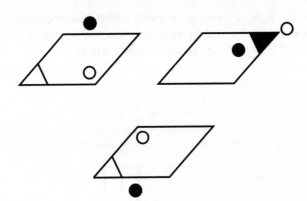

Which of the following, below, will continue
the series above?

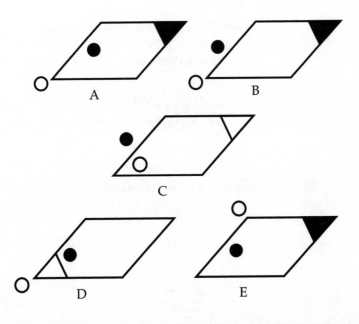

7

A man returned from his greenhouse with a small basket of cherries. To his first friend he gave half his cherries, plus half a pair of cherries, to his second he gave half of what he had left, plus half a pair of cherries, and to the third he gave half of what he had left, plus half a pair of cherries. This meant he had no cherries left. How many did he start with?

8

What word will go with the following series?

GAMMON   ACHE   TRACK   ?

A. MEAT
B. WARD
C. FIND
D. SMOOTH
E. KIND

9

TURRET is to WATCHTOWER as BASTION is to:

A. RAMPART
B. PORTCULLIS
C. COURTYARD
D. KEEP
E. DITCH

10

What number will replace the question mark?

1   2   3   7   22   ?

A. 52
B. 68
C. 126
D. 154
E. 155

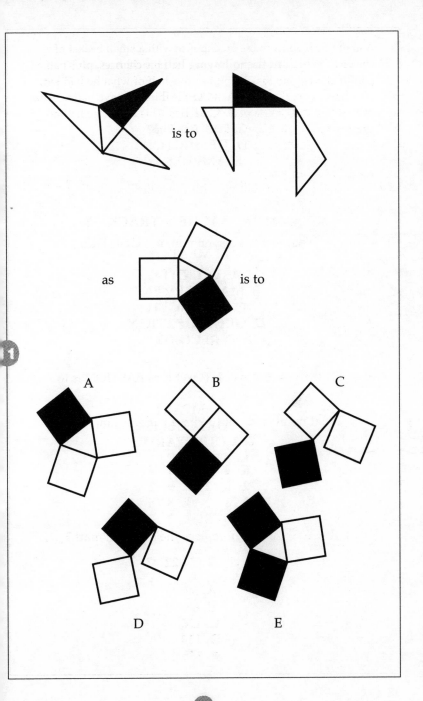

is to

as

is to

A   B   C

D   E

89

Which of the following is the odd one out?

12

A. CASKET
B. CARBOY
C. DECANTER
D. DEMIJOHN
E. AMPULLA

What word is a synonym of LOGISTICS?

13

A. VALIDITY
B. MANAGEMENT
C. STRENGTH
D. ORGANIZATION
E. RECORD

What number should replace the question mark?

14

1	7	5	9	5	7
6	4	8	1	4	4
2	3	2	?	9	2
9	1	2	3	3	5
2	6	5	4	3	7

If the missing letters in the two circles below are correctly inserted they will form antonymous words. The words do not necessarily have to be read in a clockwise direction, but the letters are in order. What are the words and missing letters?

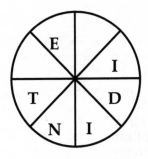 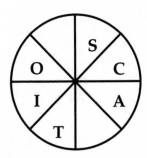

What number should replace the question mark?

91 73⅝ 56¼ 38⅞ ?

17

A word can be placed in the brackets that has the same meaning as the words outside. What is it?

VIOLIN (• • • • • •) SWINDLE

18

Which of the following is always an ingredient of CURACAO?

A. PLUMS
B. LEMON PEEL
C. ORANGE PEEL
D. CHERRIES
E. LIME

19

Find a six-letter word made up of only the following four letters?

P O
E H

Which of the following will replace the question mark and complete the series?

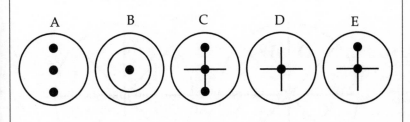

If the missing letters in the two circles below are correctly inserted they will form synonymous words. The words do not necessarily have to be read in a clockwise direction, but the letters are in order. What are the words and missing letters?

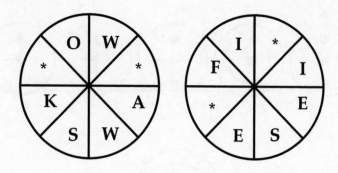

21

What number should replace the question mark?

7	5	9	18
6	3	7	21
4	3	9	?
7	4	8	24

22

What word can be placed in front of the other five to form
five new words? Each dot represents a letter.

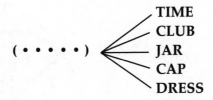

(• • • • •) < TIME
                CLUB
                JAR
                CAP
                DRESS

If the missing letters in the circle below are correctly inserted
they will form an eight-letter word. The word will not
necessarily have to be read in a clockwise direction, but the
letters are in order. What is the word and missing letters?

What word can be placed in front of the other five to form
five new words? Each dot represents a letter.

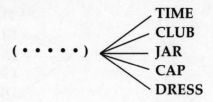

23

(• • • • •)
⟵
TIME
CLUB
JAR
CAP
DRESS

24

If the missing letters in the circle above are correctly inserted
they will form an eight-letter word. The word will not
necessarily have to be read in a clockwise direction, but the
letters are in order. What is the word and missing letters?

26

What number should replace the question mark?

2   –5⅞   –13¾   ?   –29½   –37⅜

27

What two words are antonymous?

A. GRAND
B. BALEFUL
C. ECONOMICAL
D. CLEANSE
E. SHARP
F. SULLY

28

What word is closest in meaning to feisty?

A. HOLY
B. MALEVOLENT
C. MEAN
D. GENEROUS
E. SPIRITED

29

Place two three-letter segments together to form a tree.

CHE   DEN   OAK   LOW   LIN   POP

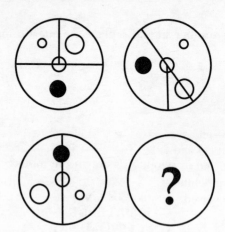

Which of the circles below will continue
the sequence above?

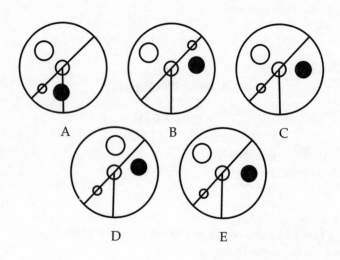

A   B   C

D   E

Answers

1 D. The others all have identical pairs: A and E, B and F, and C and G, except that black and white shading is reversed.

2 All systems go.

3 4. The sum of the inner and outer rings of diagonally opposite segments are the same. 6 + 4 = 8 + 2.

4 Abatement.

5 Profligate, parsimonious.

6 A. At each stage, the black circle rotates 90° clockwise and goes in and out of the parallelogram; the white circle rotates 90°anti- (counter) clockwise and also goes in and out of the parallelogram; the triangle rotates 180° and changes from black to white and vice versa.

7 7 pairs of cherries. He gave the 14 cherries to his friends as follows: To the first friend (half of 7) 3½ pairs + ½ a pair = 4 pairs (leaving 3 pairs).
To the second friend (half of 3) 1½ pairs + ½ a pair = 2 pairs (leaving 1 pair).
To the third friend (half of 1) ½ a pair + ½ a pair = 1 pair.

8 Ward.
Each word can be prefixed by BACK, making backgammon, backache, backtrack, and backward.

9 Keep.

10 155.
Consecutive numbers are multiplied together and 1 is added to the answer.
1 x 1 [1] + 1 = 2; 1 x 2 [2] + 1 = 3; 2 x 3 [6] + 1 = 7; 3 x 7 [21] + 1 = 22; 7 x 22 [154] + 1 = 155.

11 C. The left part transfers across to lie touching the original, uppermost right side.

12 A. Casket. It is a box, the others are jars, normally made of glass.

13 Organization.

14 6. The sum of the columns are, reading left to right: 20, 21, 22, 23, 24, 25.

15 Intrepid, cautious.
The missing letters are: R and P (intrepid) and U twice (cautious).

16 $21\frac{1}{2}$.
The number decreases by $17\frac{3}{8}$ each time.

17 Fiddle.

18 C (orange peel).

19 Hoopoe (a bird).

20 D. Different symbols in adjoining circles on the same row are carried into the circle between them in the row above. Similar symbols in the same place are dropped.

21 Waxworks, effigies.
The missing letters are X and R (waxworks) and F and G (effigies).

22 9.
Reading from left to right (first column – second column) x third column = fourth column. $(4 - 3)$ [1] x 9 = 9. The others are: $(7 - 5)$ [2] x 9 = 18; $(6 - 3)$ [3] x 7 = 21; $(7 - 4)$ [3] x 8 = 24.

23 Night.

24 Hipflask.
The missing letters are F and K.

25 A. Reading across rows and down columns, unique elements in the first two are transferred to the third (bottom or right). Common elements disappear.

26 $-21\frac{5}{8}$.
The number decreases by $7\frac{7}{8}$ each time.

27 F (sully) and D (cleanse).

28 E (Spirited).

29 Linden.

30 C. At each stage, the long line rotates 45° clockwise, the short line rotates 180° and all the circles rotate 90° clockwise.

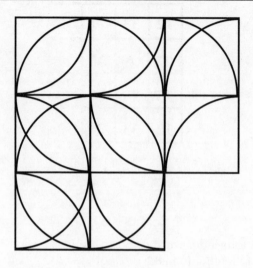

Which of the following tiles will complete the
square above?

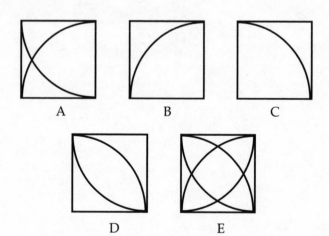

A   B   C

D   E

What number should replace the question mark?

12	33	21	12
27	?	31	27
15	25	10	15
12	33	21	12

A four-letter word can be added at the end of the
following to make five new words. What is it?

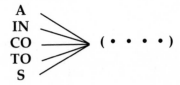

A
IN
CO
TO
S

(• • • •)

DREY is to SQUIRREL as HOLT is to:

A. OTTER
B. BADGER
C. BOAR
D. FERRET
E. MOLE

4

5

What is the value of $\frac{7}{9} \div \frac{1}{3}$?

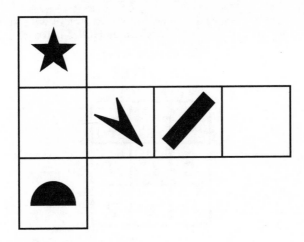

When the above is folded into a cube, only one of the
following can be produced. Which one is it?

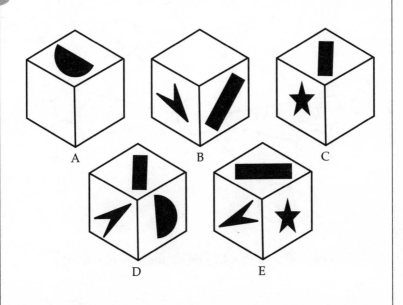

Start at a corner square and move in a clockwise spiral to the middle to spell out a nine-letter word. What are the missing letters?

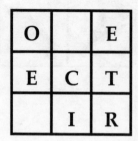

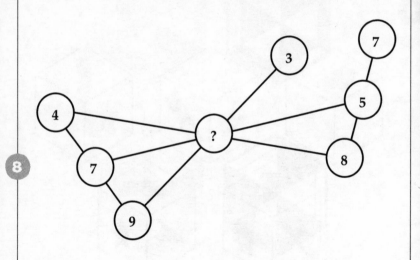

What number should replace the question mark?

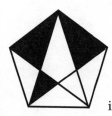 is to  as  is to

A

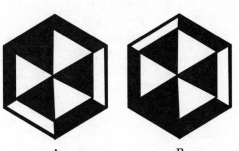

B

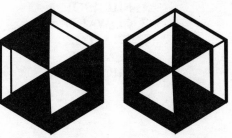

C

D

10

Two American soldiers meet on a bridge. One is the father of the other one's son. What is their relationship?

What two words are antonymous?

A. ONEROUS
B. EFFICACIOUS
C. FIRM
D. SAD
E. UNAVAILING
F. CORRUPT

11

What word is the odd one out?

A. MILKSOP
B. COWARD
C. TRAITOR
D. CAITIFF
E. NAMBY-PAMBY

12

What number should replace the question mark?

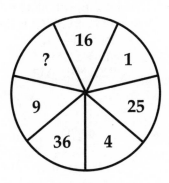

A. 46
B. 45
C. 47
D. 49
E. 0

What two words are closest in meaning?

A. HASTY
B. INDIRECTLY
C. CARELESSLY
D. OBLIQUELY
E. CAREFULLY
F. SLICK

What word is the odd one out?

A. REGENERATE
B. REGURGITATE
C. REVITALIZE
D. RESUSCITATE
E. REANIMATE

What number should replace the question mark?

5   1   2½   2½   0   4   −2½   ?

A word can be placed in the brackets that has the
same meaning as the words outside. Each dot
represents a letter. What is it?

MANAGER (• • • •)   PROTRUSION

110

What number should replace the question mark?

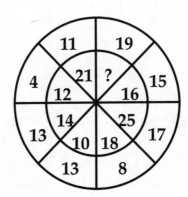

Which of the following is not a type of wind?

A. MISTRAL
B. PAVANE
C. ZEPHYR
D. SIROCCO
E. MONSOON

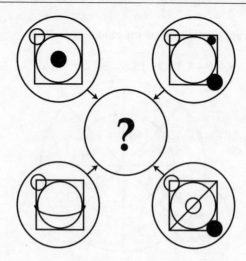

Each line and symbol that appears in the four outer circles, above, is transferred to the middle circle according how many times it appears, as follows:

One time — it is transferred
Two times — it is possibly transferred
Three times — it is transferred
Four times — it is not transferred

Which of the circles below should appear in the middle circle?

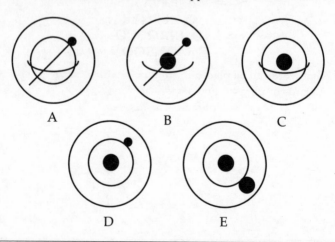

Place two three-letter segments together to form a coin.

KOP   UDO   PIA   RUP   ESC   LIR

What number should replace the question mark?

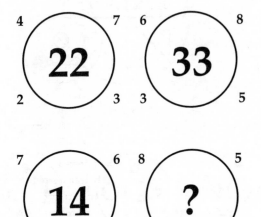

What word can be placed in front of the other five to form five new words or phrases, and some words may be hyphenated? Each dot represents a letter.

(• • • • •) ⟨ **GLAZED**
TAKE
PARK
CROSS
ENTRY

If the missing letters in the circle below are correctly inserted they will form an eight-letter word. The word will not necessarily have to be read in a clockwise direction, but the letters are in order. What is the word and missing letters?

If 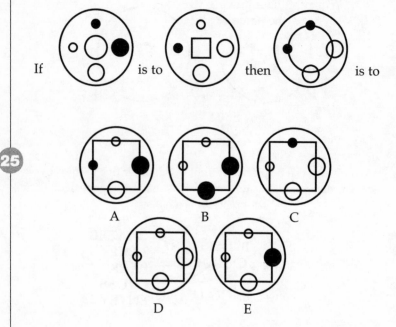 is to ... then ... is to

A   B   C

D   E

If the missing letters in the two circles below are correctly inserted they will form synonymous words. The words do not necessarily have to be read in a clockwise direction, but the letters are in order. What are the words and missing letters?

26

Which of the following words is not a group noun (the name of a group of objects)?

A. COVEY
B. SIEGE
C. SHIELD
D. SKULK
E. CLOWDER

27

What word is an antonym of NOCUOUS?

A. SYSTEMATIC
B. PAROCHIAL
C. HARMLESS
D. MERCURIAL
E. TRAUMATIC

28

Simplify the following and find x?

$$\frac{64 - 32}{^1/_8 - ^1/_{16}} = x$$

Which of the circles below will continue the sequence above?

A B C

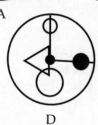 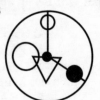

D E

Answers

Test **Four**

1 C. Reading across columns and down rows, unique elements in the first two are transferred to the third (bottom or right). Common elements disappear.

2 58. Looking across each row and down each column, the third and fourth numbers are the differences of the numbers in the two previous squares.

3 Ward. The words made are: award, inward, coward, toward, and sward.

4 Otter. A holt is an otter's home as a drey is a squirrel's home.

5 $2\frac{1}{3}$.
The sum can be rephrased as $\frac{7}{9} \times \frac{3}{1}$ (or 3); $3 \times \frac{7}{9} = 2\frac{1}{9}$ (or $2\frac{1}{3}$).

6 A.

7 Geometric.
The missing letters are G and M.

8 8.
The sum of each line of three digits comes to 20.

9 B. The two figures are mirror images of each other.

10 They are the son's mother and father.

11 B (efficacious) and E (unavailing).

12 C (traitor).

13 D (49).
Alternate sectors increase by 1, 3, 5, 7, 9, 11, and 13. They are also squares of 1, 2, 3, 4, 5, 6, and 7.

14 B (indirectly) and D (obliquely).

15 B (regurgitate, to vomit). The others are to restore or revive

16 5½.
There are two series that alternate:
one is – 2½, the other is + 1½.
Looking at the two series separately,
– 2½ runs 5, 2½, 0, –2½;
+ 1½ goes 1, 2½, 4, 5½.

17 Boss.

18 16.
The sum of inner and diagonally opposite outer segments totals 29.

19 Pavane (a dance).

20 B.

21 Escudo.

22 12.
In each case (top left x top right) – (bottom left x bottom right) = middle. (8 x 5) [40] – (7 x 4) [28] = 12.
The others are:
(7 x 4) [28] – (2 x 3) [6] = 22;
(6 x 8) [48] – (3 x 5) [15] = 33;
(7 x 6) [42] – (4 x 7) [28] = 14.

23 Double.

24 Hijacker.
The missing letters are J and K.

25 E.
The circle becomes a square; a black circle on the top becomes white; and black and white swap left to right.

26 Ointment and liniment.
The missing letters are: O and M (ointment) and L and M (liniment).

27 Shield. The others are a covey of pheasants, grouse, quail or partridges; a siege of cranes or herons; a skulk of foxes; and a clowder of cats.

28 C (harmless).

29 512. 64 – 32 [32] ÷ ⅛ (²⁄₁₆) – ¹⁄₁₆ [¹⁄₁₆] can be rephrased as 32 x ¹⁶⁄₁ (16) = 512.

30 C. At each stage, the triangle rotates 180°, the large circle rotates 90° clockwise, the small white circle rotates 45° anti- (counter) clockwise, and the black circle rotates 90° anti- (counter) clockwise.

Test Five

Four of the five pieces below can be fitted together to form a perfect square. What piece is the odd one out?

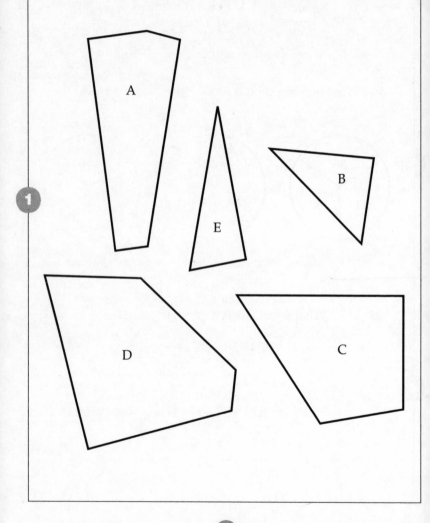

ANGER   TENDER   DIRECT   RENTED   RANGE

What word is missing from above?

A. GREEN
B. FINAL
C. CREDIT
D. TRAIN
E. DETECT

What number should replace the question mark?

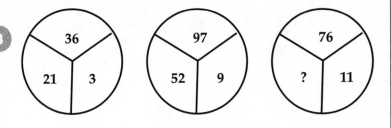

What word is a synonym of rectitude?

A. CORRUPTION
B. REDRESS
C. RESTORATION
D. HONESTY
E. REINSTATEMENT

5 Bill's house is 10th from one end of the block and sixth from the other end. How many houses are there in the block?

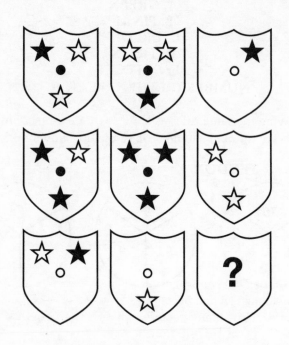

6

Which shield, below, will replace the question mark above?

A   B   C   D   E

A three-word phrase, below, has had each word's initial letter removed. What is the phrase?

OATCHN

NUMBER (RETURN) LETTER

Following the same rules as above, what word should go in the brackets?

TENDON (• • • • • •) LILIES

Out of 100 people surveyed, 86 had an egg for breakfast, 75 had bacon, 62 had toast, and 82 had coffee. How many people, as least, must have had all four items?

What letter is immediately to the left of the letter three to the right of the letter immediately to the left of the letter three to the right of the letter B?

A B C D E F G H

Which of the following is the odd one out?

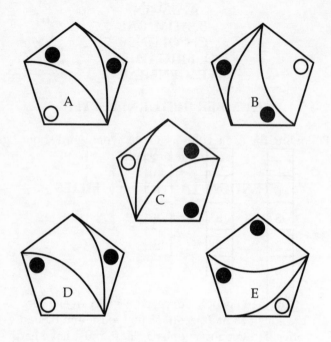

11

What two words are antonymous?

A. NOVITIATE
B. SLOW
C. CLOSE
D. EXOTIC
E. EXPERT
F. APPREHENSIVE

12

What is the odd one out?

A. MAJOR
B. ADMIRAL
C. COLONEL
D. BRIGADIER
E. GENERAL

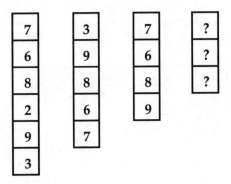

Which of the boxes below will follow the
sequence above?

8	7	7	9	9
7	9	8	7	8
9	8	9	8	7
A	B	C	D	E

A   B   C

D   E

Into which of the boxes A, B, C, D, or E, can a dot be placed so that both dots will meet the same conditions as in the top box?

A word can be placed in the brackets that has the same meaning as the words outside. What is it?

PENALTY (• • • •)   EXCELLENT

What number should replace the question mark?

7 –5 2 1 –3 7 –8 13 ? 19

Place two three-letter segments together to form a profession.

BUR SOL GAR DEN SAR VAN

What word can be placed in front of the other five to form five new words or phrases? Each dot represents a letter.

(• • • •)

TABLE
UP
TAIL
PIKE
OVER

Each of the nine squares in the grid marked 1A to 3C should incorporate all of the items which are shown in the squares of the same letter and number, at the left and top, respectively. For example, 2B should incorporate all of the symbols that are in squares 2 and B. One square, however, is incorrect. Which one is it?

Find a six-letter word made up of only the following four letters?

T E
P O

What number should replace the question mark?

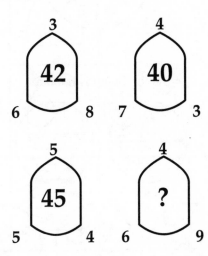

What is a LEMAN?

A. A PARAMOUR
B. AN ANIMAL
C. A NOOSE
D. A BODICE
E.. A SPINNAKER

If the missing letters in the circle below are correctly inserted they will form an eight-letter word. The word will not necessarily have to be read in a clockwise direction, but the letters are in order. What is the word and missing letters?

Which of the following is the odd one out?

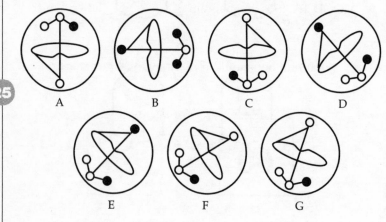

A B C D

E F G

What word is a synonym of bathos?

A. DIFFIDENCE
B. SUBMARINE
C. MAWKISHNESS
D. GRACE
E. SHIELD

If the missing letters in the two circles below are correctly inserted they will form synonymous words. The words do not necessarily have to be read in a clockwise direction, but the letters are in order. What are the words and missing letters?

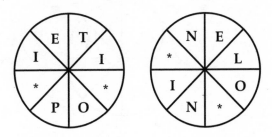

MOOD TANS is an anagram of what eight-letter word?

What number should replace the question mark?

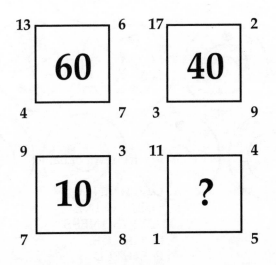

Which of the circles A, B, C, D, or E, should replace
the question mark below?

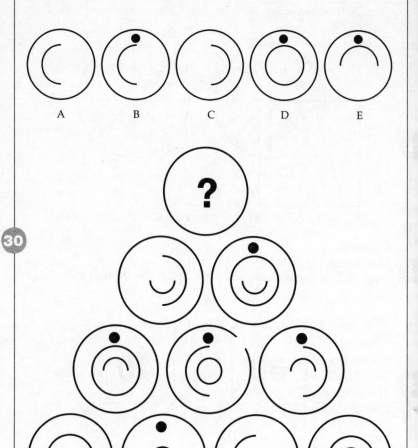

A   B   C   D   E

Answers

C.

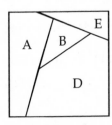

C (credit).
Credit is an anagram of direct as is anger of range, and tender is of rented.

21. In each case (top —left) ÷ 5 = right.
(76 – 21) [55] ÷ 5 = 11.
The others are:
(36 – 21) [15] ÷ 5 = 3;
(97 – 52) [45] ÷ 5 = 9.

Honesty.

15.

B.
Reading across columns and down rows of shields, common elements with the same shading in the first two are transferred to the third (bottom or right) and change shading. Unique elements disappear.

To catch on.

Silent. Three letters of the left and right words transfer to the middle as follows:

T	E	N	D	O	N
6	4				5

(S	I	L	E	N	T)
1	2	3	4	5	6

L	I	L	I	E	S
	2	3			1

5. Add the differences between 100 and 86, 75, 62 and 82, then subtract this total from the original 100.
(14 + 25 + 38 + 18) = 95;
100 – 95 = 5.

10 F.

11 D. The others all have identical pairs: A and B, and C and E.

12 A (novitiate) and E (expert).

13 B (admiral, a naval rank). The others are all army ranks.

14 E. The order of the column is reversed and the lowest digit is removed each time.

15 D.
One dot will appear in a enclosed small circle and another in the link between two larger circles.

16 Fine.

17 –13. There are two alternate series,
– 5 and + 6. The numbers are: 7, 2, –3, –8, –13; –5, 1, 7, 13, 19.

18 Bursar.

19 Turn.

20 1C.

21 Poppet, teepee, or the mexican dishes totopo or topote.

22 60. The sums are:
(top x left) + (top x right) = middle.
(4 x 6) [24] + (4 x 9) [36] = 60.
Others are:
(3 x 6) [18] + (3 x 8) [24] = 42;
(4 x 7) [28] + (4 x 3) [12] = 40;
(5 x 5) [25] + (5 x 4) [20] = 45.

23 A (a paramour).

24 Gangrene.
The missing letter is G twice.

25 B. The others all have identical pairs: A and C, D and E, and F and G.

26 C (mawkishness).

27 Impolite and insolent.
The missing letters are: M and L (impolite) and S and T (insolent).

Mastodon.

30. The sums are: (top left
– bottom right) x (bottom
left + top right) = middle.
(11 – 5) [6] x (1 + 4) [5] = 30.
Others are:
(13 – 7) [6] x (4 + 6) [10] = 60;
(17 – 9) [8] x (3 + 2) [5] = 40;
(9 – 8) [1] x (7 + 3) [10] = 10.

B. Different symbols/lines
in adjoining circles on the
same row are carried into the
circle between them in the
row above. Similar symbols/
lines in the same place are
dropped.

What comes next in this sequence?

A   B   C

D   E

What two words are antonyms?

A. BARE
B. TINY
C. SAFE
D. PRODIGIOUS
E. ABUSIVE
F. FRUGAL

What number is the odd one out?

A. 382618
B. 589411
C. 213787
D. 528572
E. 654346

Find the starting point and move from square to adjoining square, horizontally or vertically, but not diagonally, to spell a 12-letter word, using each letter once only. What are the missing letters?

A		P
R	T	O
N	I	L
I	S	

Simile is to likeness as onomatopoeia is to:

A. REPETITION
B. SOUND
C. VERSION
D. UNDERSTATEMENT
E. EXAGGERATION

5

Which of the following is the odd one out?

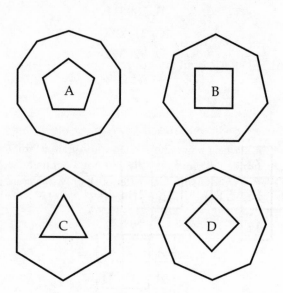

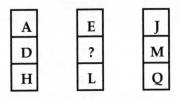

7

What letter should replace the question mark?

What number comes next in this sequence?

1 3 8 19 42 ?

8

9

HALTED CAR is an anagram of what nine-letter word?

10

	72	
46	16	51
	34	

	96	
38	18	43
	12	

	28	
14	?	16
	11	

What number should replace the question mark?

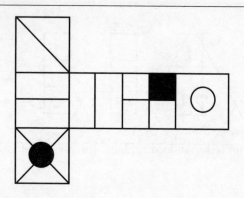

When the above is folded to form a cube, just one of the following below can be produced. What one is it?

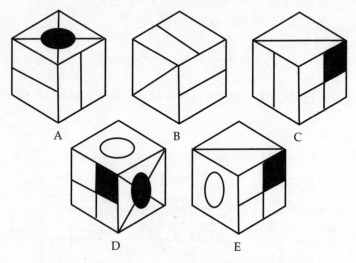

A   B   C

D   E

What two words are synonymous?

A. PENALTY
B. HINT
C. REQUEST
D. ENTREAT
E. MOTIVE
F. MAXIMUM

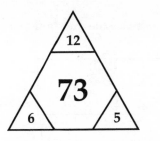

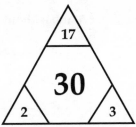

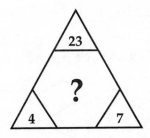

13

What number should replace the question mark?

14

What is the odd one out?

A. BARBICAN
B. MINSTER
C. CITADEL
D. FORTRESS
E. STRONGHOLD

15

Find two words with different spellings, but which sound alike, that can mean:

PORTICO / WALK

16

What number should replace the question mark?

22   14¼   6½   ?   –9

17

Insert a word in the brackets that completes the first word and starts the second one. Each dot represents a letter.

TRAM (• • • •)   AGE

18

Place two three-letter segments together to form a vehicle.

TER   WAY   SKY   DRO   VER   CAR

19

A word can be placed in the brackets that has the same meaning as the words outside. What is it?

AVERAGE (• • • •)   STINGY

Which of the hexagons at the bottom, A, B, C, D, or E, should replace the question mark below?

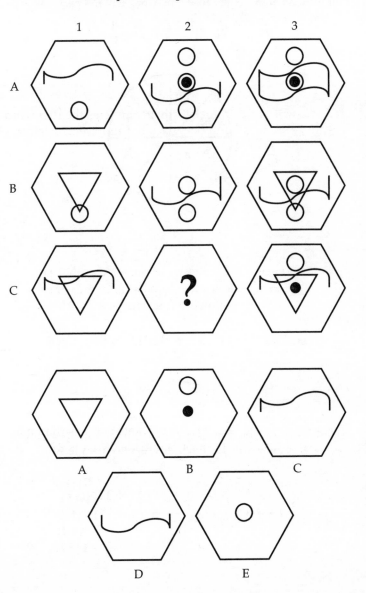

If the missing letters in the circle below are correctly inserted they will form an eight-letter word. The word will not necessarily have to be read in a clockwise direction, but the letters are in order. What is the word and missing letters?

21

Find a six-letter word made up of only the following four letters.

L E
O G

22

What word can be placed in front of the other five to form five new words? Each dot represents a letter.

23

(• • • • •)

BREAD
FALL
HAND
AGE
LIST

What number should replace the question mark?

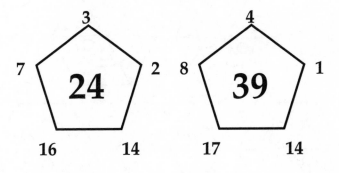

Which of the following is the odd one out?

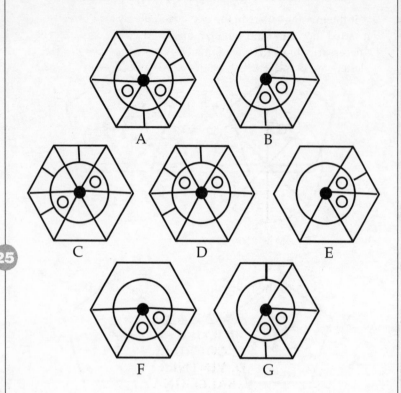

26   NEAR BUMP is an anagram of what eight-letter word?

If the missing letters in the two circles below are correctly inserted they will form synonymous words. The words do not necessarily have to be read in a clockwise direction, but the letters are in order. What are the words and missing letters?

27

 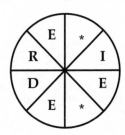

Which of the following is not an occupation?

A. VESPIARY
B. BAILIFF
C. COURIER
D. VINTNER
E. BALLERINA

28

What is a GIMCRACK?

A. BLOW
B. BAUBLE
C. JAUNTY
D. CRACKER
E. PRESS

29

Which of the circles below should replace the question mark below?

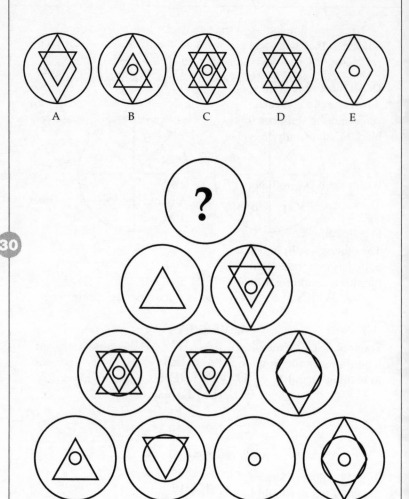

A   B   C   D   E

30

Answers

1 D. All three shapes move down one place at each stage and the star goes from black to white and vice versa.

2 B (tiny) and D (prodigious).

3 D (528572).
The others, if split in half and added as two three-digits numbers, would total 1000.
$528 + 572 = 1100$.

4 Trampolinist. The missing letters are, reading from top to bottom: M and T.

5 Sound.

6 B. The number of sides of the inner figure should be half those of the outer ones. In the case of B, there is a square inside a seven-sided figure.

7 H.
Reading down each column, the letter advances three, then four places in the alphabet. Reading across, the difference is four, then five places.

8 89.
Double the previous number, then add 1, 2, 3, 4, and 5, respectively.

9 Cathedral.

10 12.
The sum of digits of the left and right numbers and also the top and bottom ones equals the middle number.
$1 + 4 + 1 + 6 = 12$; $2 + 8 + 1 + 1 = 12$.

11 C.

12 C (request) and D (entreat).

13 88.
The sum is: left^2 + right^2 + top = middle.
4^2 [16] + 7^2 [49] + 23 = 88.
Others are:
6^2 [36] + 5^2 [25] + 12 = 73;
2^2 [4] + 3^2 [9] + 17 = 30.

14 B (minster). The rest are types of military buildings; a minster is a religious one.

15 Gate and gait.

16 $-11\frac{1}{4}$. Subtract $7\frac{3}{4}$ at each stage.

17 Line.

18 Drosky (a Russian two- or four-wheeled cart).

19 Mean.

20 B. Reading across columns and down rows, unique elements in the first two are transferred to the third (bottom or right). Common elements disappear.

21 Tribunal.
The missing letters are T and B.

22 Goggle or, of course, Google, the search giant.

23 Short.

24 48.
The sums are (bottom left – bottom right) x (sum of top three numbers) = middle.
(11 – 7) [4] x (4 + 3 + 5) [12] = 48.
Others are:
(16 – 14) [2] x (7 + 3 + 2) [12] = 24;
(17 – 14) [3] x (8 + 4 + 1) [13] = 39;
(20 – 18) [2] x (9 + 7 + 2) [18] = 36.

25 C. The others all have identical pairs: A and D, B and G, and E and F.

26 Penumbra.

27 Imposter and deceiver.
The missing letters are P and T (imposter) and C and V (deceiver).

28 A (vespiary, a wasp's nest).

29 B (bauble).

30 C.
Different symbols in adjoining
circles on the same row are
carried into the circle between
them in the row above.
Similar symbols in the same
place are dropped.

Test Seven

ROWS   (SOFTWARE)   FATE
?   (COMPLETE)   MELT

Which word below should replace the question mark above?

1

A. COME
B. POET
C. COPE
D. LOPE
E. CODE

ISLAND : WATER

Which pair of words below have the same relationship
as the words above?

2

A. ORCHARD : TREES
B. MEADOW : GRASS
C. BOOK : SHELF
D. OASIS : SAND
E. HEM : FRINGE

What word is an antonym of ARISTOCRATIC?

A. UNKIND
B. PATRICIAN
C. LIBERAL
D. POOR
E. PLEBIAN

3

4 How many minutes is it before 10.00 pm if, 50 minutes ago, it was four times as many minutes past 7.00 pm?

5

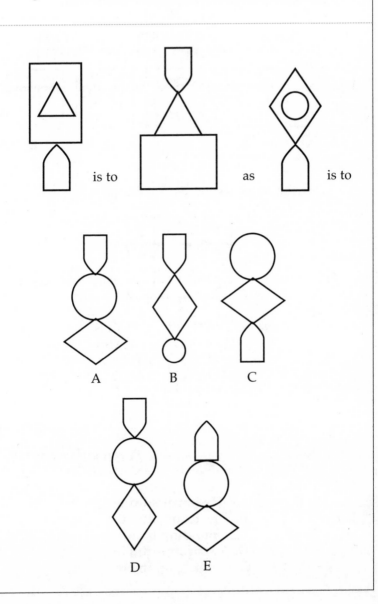

is to   as   is to

A   B   C

D   E

6 Which of the five boxes below is most like the box above?

A   B   C   D   E

What number should replace the question mark?

7	4	9	2
3	1	1	3
4	7	6	5
2	2	?	4

7

A. 0
B. 1
C. 2
D. 3
E. 4

What would describe STERNUTATION?

A. Heavy breathing
B. The act of sneezing
C. Shouting loudly
D. A strict upbringing
E. Bringing up the rear

8

154

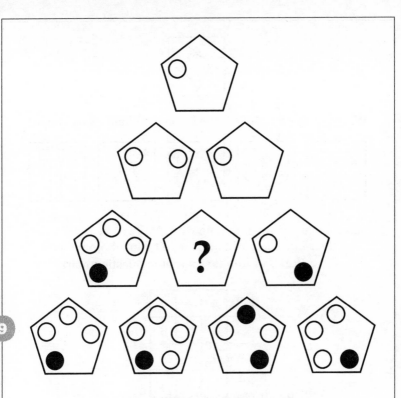

Which of the pentagons below will replace the question mark above?

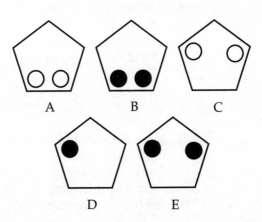

A   B   C

D   E

9

```
                A
            A   S   A
        A   S   N   S   A
    A   S   N   E   N   S   A
A   S   N   E   M   E   N   S   A
    A   S   N   E   N   S   A
        A   S   N   S   A
            A   S   A
                A
```

In how many ways can the word MENSA be read? Start at the central letter M and move to an adjoining letter vertically or horizontally, but not diagonally.

10

7240	:	95
2456	:	37

Which pair of numbers below have the same relationship as the numbers above?

A.	8056	:	98
B.	3216	:	42
C.	4824	:	36
D.	9872	:	108
E.	7218	:	94

11

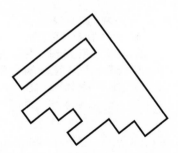

Which of the shapes below, when fitted to the piece above, will form a perfect square?

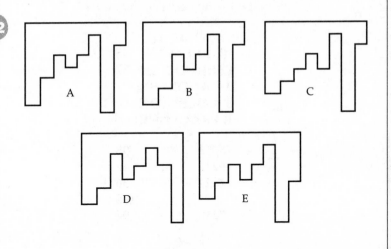

A

B

C

D

E

What word is the odd one out?

13

A. VERIFY
B. MONITOR
C. AUTHENTICATE
D. SUBSTANTIATE
E. VALIDATE

Find two words with different spellings, but which sound alike, that can mean:

14

BOUNTY / MEDDLES

What two words are synonymous?

15

A. FRACAS
B. PALAVER
C. SKIRMISH
D. PAROXYSM
E. COERCION
F. FRACTURE

What number should replace the question mark?

$$2 \quad -\tfrac{1}{3} \quad \tfrac{1}{18} \quad ? \quad \tfrac{1}{648}$$

16

A. $\tfrac{1}{108}$
B. $\tfrac{1}{324}$
C. $-\tfrac{1}{324}$
D. $-\tfrac{1}{108}$
E. $\tfrac{1}{36}$

158

Place two three-letter segments together to form an
item of clothing.

ORA TER GOT ROS FED RUF

If the missing letters in the circle below are correctly inserted
they will form an eight-letter word. The word will not
necessarily have to be read in a clockwise direction, but the
letters are in order. What is the word and missing letters?

What word can be placed in front of the other five to form
five new words? Each dot represents a letter.

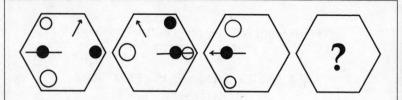

Which of the hexagons below should replace the
question mark above?

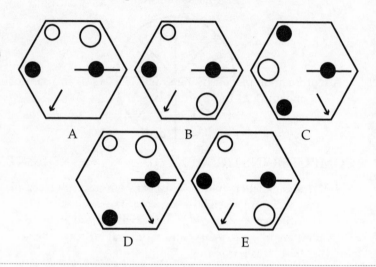

A   B   C

D   E

If the missing letters in the two circles below are correctly inserted
they will form synonymous words. The words do not necessarily
have to be read in a clockwise direction, but the letters are in
order. What are the words and missing letters?

What word is a synonym of RAILLERY?

A. CENSURE
B. SHELVES
C. FENCING
D. BANTER
E. VEHEMENCE

A word can be placed in the brackets that has the same meaning as the words outside. What is it?

COMPUTER INSTRUMENT (• • • • •) RODENT

What is the odd one out?

A. BEETLE
B. BEE
C. WASP
D. SPIDER
E. ANT

Which of the circles, A, B, C, D, or E, should replace the question mark below?

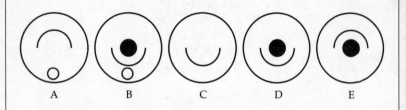

A B C D E

25

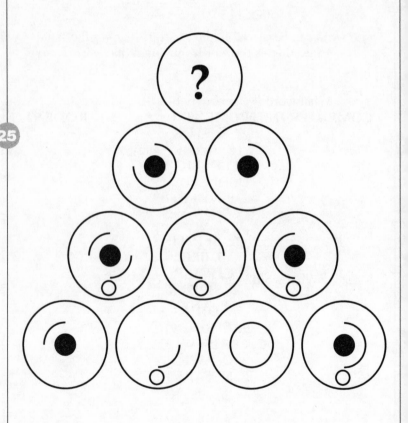

Find a six-letter word made up of only the following four letters?

O W
L I

What is the value of x?

$(3 \times 14 \div 2) + 6 + 56 = x$

What word is a synonym of LUCUBRATION?

A. STUDY
B. OIL
C. DELIGHT
D. DECEPTION
E. PERCEPTION

What word is an antonym of HEINOUS?

A. ODIOUS
B. ATROCIOUS
C. PRAISEWORTHY
D. AWFUL
E. NEFARIOUS

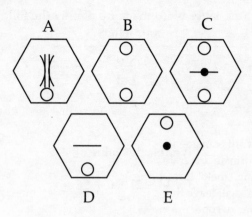

Which of the hexagons above should
replace the question mark below?

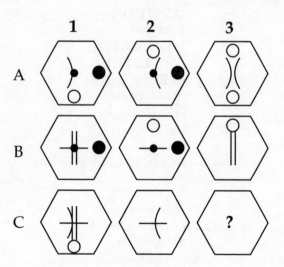

Answers

Test Seven

1 C (cope).
The two words outside the brackets form an anagram so removing "melt" from "complete" will leave the letters to make cope.

2 D (oasis : sand).
Sand entirely surrounds an oasis as water surrounds an island.

3 E (plebian).

4 26 minutes.

5 A.
The top two items separate; the larger one rotates 90° clockwise and moves to the bottom, and the smaller one becomes large and goes in the middle. The bottom item rotates 180° and moves to the top.

6 C.
It is the only one with vertical, horizontal, and diagonal symmetry.

7 A (0).
The sum of the two left columns is the same as the sum of the two right columns. Also, the 1st and 3rd columns have the same values as do the 2nd and 4th columns. The same applies to the rows.

8 B (the act of sneezing).

9 C.
Identical symbols, including shading, in adjoining pentagons on the same row are carried into the pentagon between them in the row above. Different symbols in the same place are dropped.

10 60 ways.

11 B (3216 : 42).
The left pair of digits and the right pair of digits on the left number are both divided by eight to give the digits of the right number.

12 B.

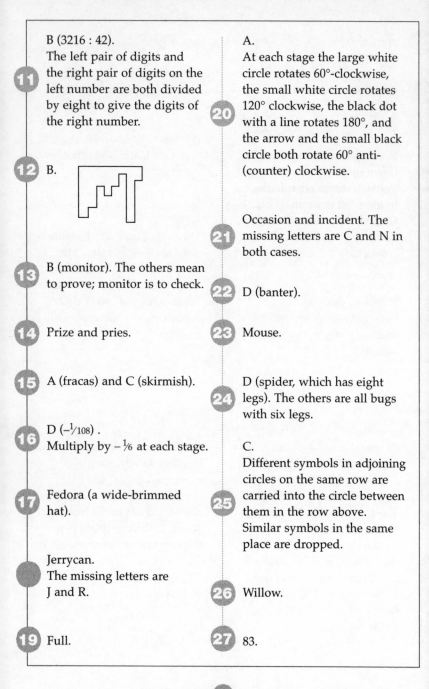

13 B (monitor). The others mean to prove; monitor is to check.

14 Prize and pries.

15 A (fracas) and C (skirmish).

16 D ($-\frac{1}{108}$).
Multiply by $-\frac{1}{6}$ at each stage.

17 Fedora (a wide-brimmed hat).

18 Jerrycan.
The missing letters are J and R.

19 Full.

20 A.
At each stage the large white circle rotates 60°-clockwise, the small white circle rotates 120° clockwise, the black dot with a line rotates 180°, and the arrow and the small black circle both rotate 60° anti-(counter) clockwise.

21 Occasion and incident. The missing letters are C and N in both cases.

22 D (banter).

23 Mouse.

24 D (spider, which has eight legs). The others are all bugs with six legs.

25 C.
Different symbols in adjoining circles on the same row are carried into the circle between them in the row above. Similar symbols in the same place are dropped.

26 Willow.

27 83.

166

28 A (study).

29 C (praiseworthy).

30 A.
Reading across columns and down rows, unique elements in the first two are transferred to the third (bottom or right). Common elements disappear.

Developing learning skills

Does the prospect of learning a foreign language or trying to master the latest piece of equipment at work fill you with apprehension? The first step in overcoming this is to develop confidence in yourself. Learning anything new often seems daunting, but telling yourself that you cannot possibly do it is the guaranteed route to failure.

If you think about the impressive range of skills that you possess, you will realize that it is only your own anxieties that are holding you back. The skills that you use from day to day may seem very ordinary, but in fact they represent a vast amount of knowledge that you have already taken in your stride. Answering the questions below should help to make you more aware of your enormous learning potential.

1. Can you walk?

2. Can you talk?

3. Can you distinguish between different shapes/sounds/textures and so on?

4. Are you numerate and literate, even at the most elementary level?

5. Can you make a cup of coffee?

6. Can you cook?

7. If not, do you know how to order a takeaway?

8. Can you go out and buy a loaf of bread?

9. Can you cross the road safely?

10. Do you have a fairly clear idea of your likes and dislikes?

11. Can you communicate these to others?

12. Do you have any hobbies? Think about the skills, however basic, that you need for these.

13. Do you know any words of a foreign language?

14. Can you drive?

15. If not, are you familiar with other public or private means of getting around?

16. Have you ever taken on any kind of work, either paid or voluntary?

17. Are you familiar with any technological equipment, from telephones and hi-fis to the Internet?

18. Can you change a plug, or know who to contact if you can't?

19. Can you name ten other countries?

20. Can you name the President of the USA?

These questions should have highlighted the wide range of skills and information that you have acquired since birth – simply surviving from day to day requires a continuous cycle of learning. Now turn to the following tests to give yourself an idea of just how good your learning abilities are.

How Does it Work?

Study the instructions for the various imaginary gadgets listed below. After 10 minutes, turn the page and attempt the multiple-choice questions to discover how much information has registered.

1. The Ho-hum

To operate safely, only remove the protective shield when cutting is in progress. Align the heel at the appropriate foot-size mark and set the gender dial. When all is in place, raise the shield and activate the red button. The blue dial controls the degree of nail trim. Activating the green button switches the Ho-hum off, and automatically lowers the shield, after a 10-second period, to allow for foot removal.

2. The Didgerer

The Didgerer is not suitable for use in very confined spaces. To operate, aim the pointed end towards the animal, ideally within a distance of 12 feet to guarantee accuracy. Click the protruding end in, while still pointing toward the animal to activate the sensory device. Releasing the end at any time results in the catcher being automatically wound in. The Didgerer is effective with both still and moving creatures, with minimal trauma.

3. The Doodar

Switch the Doodar on after ensuring that all 5 batteries are correctly in place. Using the arrow keys, highlight the 6 adjectives characterizing your current mood from the Trait List appearing on screen. Finally, move the cursor to "All" to register your mood and to display a choice of aromatic remedies. After detailing your current location as prompted, a list of outlets supplying the aromatherapy oils is displayed, with details of stock levels. After use, simply switch off.

4. The Whatsitsname

Having produced your chosen culinary mixture, set the white Whatsitsname gauge to the switch that is relevant to the mixture, e.g. cake base, savoury sauce etc. Place the sterilized Whatsitsname into the mixture, and stir for 5 seconds. Remove and wipe to determine the exact amount of thickening agent (provided) required to produce the perfect consistency. Place in the sterilizer before further use in order to clean and reset the device.

5. The Heebie-jeeby

Using the suction pads, attach a Heebie-jeeby centrally on each window after leaving the vehicle during cold weather, particularly at night. Place the rectangular Heebie-jeebies on the front and rear windscreens, and the square Heebie-jeebies on the smaller side windows. To activate, turn the circular switch on each one clockwise until the arrow is level with the orange dot. Remove when using the vehicle, whose windows will be frost-free. When the switch is jammed towards the yellow dot, recharging is necessary.

Questions

1 How many adjectives are used to describe your mood on the Doodar?
a) 8 b) 5 c) 6 d) 7 e) 4

2 What gadget is used in connection with animals?
a) Whatsitsname b) Heeby-jeeby c) Ho-hum d) Didgerer e) Doodar

3 What controls the degree of nail trim on one of the gadgets?
a) a blue button b) a blue switch c) a green switch d) a blue dial
e) a green button

4 Where should you not use the Didgerer?
a) in a car b) in a ballroom c) in a park d) in a department store
e) on a mountain

5 Which of the following is a named feature of the Ho-hum?
a) suction pads b) protective shield c) white gauge
d) battery-operated mechanism e) sensory device

6 What shape should the gadget that sits on the rear windscreen be?
a) circular b) triangular c) rectangular d) square e) irregular

7 What is used to reset the Whatsitsname?
a) a cleanser b) a dial c) a white gauge d) a green button e) a sterilizer

8 What must be detailed to register a list of outlets on one of the gadgets?
a) your current geographical location b) your foot-size c) your home
address d) your current mood e) your car

9 How should the switch on the Heeby-jeeby be activated?
a) pressed in b) turned clockwise c) clicked d) pulled out e) pushed up

10 Within how many feet should the Didgerer be operated?
a) 6 b) 15 c) 8 d) 10 e) 12

Finding the Right Words

Study this list of words and accompanying definitions for 5 minutes only – efficient learning is related to speed. Then turn the page, look at the two lists of definitions and words that follow, and match them up. Beware of the red herrings! The test definitions are worded differently from those in the first list, which means that the ability to learn and understand, and not just a good memory, are vital to do well. Of course, if you are already familiar with any of the words, you will have to account for this when scoring.

Lamellibranch: animal of the mollusc class

Eupepsia: good digestion

Afrormosia: African teaklike wood

Riparian: inhabiting or situated on a river bank

Nidifugous: (of birds) leaving their nest soon after being hatched

Imbroglio: confused state of affairs

Nagelfluh: Swiss or Italian conglomerate rock

Guaiacum: South-American tree whose components are medicinal

Now cover up and get matching!

Definitions:

1 Pertaining to a slope by water

2 Hard, yellow-brown plant material

3 Young fledgling active at an early age

4 Soft-bodied animal with a hard shell

5 Perplexing situation

6 Large plant bearing therapeutic properties

7 The satisfactory processing of food in the stomach

8 European coarse-grained mineral matter

Pick out which of these words match the above definitions:

(a) Gualica	(f) Eupepsicum	(k) Riparian
(b) Nagelfluh	(g) Riparicer	(l) Eupepsia
(c) Imbroglio	(h) Imbragsia	(m) Lamellibranch
(d) Samelibranch	(i) Nidifugous	(n) Guaiacum
(e) Afrormosia	(j) Bagelflew	

These kinds of tests give you a good general idea of your ability to learn, and yet they cannot tell the whole story. Learning is a complex process and your capacity to digest, retain and recall information is greatly influenced by the situation you find yourself in, and the way in which information is presented to you.

Early Influences

Our ability and desire to learn stems predominantly from our childhood. Learning to walk and talk is largely a matter of mirroring and repetition, so the degree of encouragement and attention that you receive has a huge influence on your early progress. Anyone with a younger brother or sister will no doubt remember how annoyed they sometimes felt about being constantly copied. Only later in life do we realize just how valuable this learning process is.

From birth onwards, we learn through a continual cycle of habituation – getting used to something – and readjustment. A baby's initial encounter with anything new is often greeted with terror. Only reassurance and closer examination will reveal that the rocking horse, for example, really is harmless.

All of us have a deep-seated desire to question the world around us. As children, "why?" is a key word in our vocabulary. Unfortunately, the path of learning is too often blocked by other people's negative responses – what can any child learn from being told "because it does"? Criticism is equally harmful. If a child is told that his or her handwriting is dreadful, that child may well take this as a direct attack on their personality. This  could seriously damage their confidence, and consequently dampen further motivation to learn. What is needed, for children and adults alike, is positive encouragement and ways of teaching that clearly separate someone's personality from the skills they are trying to master. With this approach, our learning skills should flourish, from birth right through to our mature years.

There are other influences from our early years that affect our attitude toward learning in later life. Fond memories of being read to, or helped to read, at bedtime often means that reading is subconsciously linked with pleasure. This could be the start of a lifelong love of reading, which will undoubtedly help to make us more efficient learners.

What is Learning?

The information we take in when we are reading is stored in the many millions of cells that make up the human brain. These cells are connected by a vast network of pathways known as dentritic spines. Acquiring new knowledge doesn't mean that the brain gets too "full" and information is lost in some way – instead, it causes the brain to develop additional pathways. Put simply, the more you learn, the more you are able to learn.

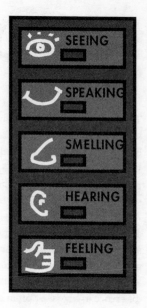

Each of us learns in different ways. For example, ask a friend to observe you discretely at some point in the future when you are in the middle of a discussion. You must be unaware of this, so that you act in a perfectly natural way. How do your mannerisms and facial expressions change when you are asked a question, and when you are listening? What happens to your eyes?

Some people believe that close observation of how your eyes move when you are interacting with others can reveal the way in which you prefer to learn and process information. If your eyes dart upward when you are asked a question or are trying to remember something, you could be someone who responds well to visual images. This is thought to be because you are glancing toward the top of the head which, roughly speaking, is where the eyes are located.

This tendency might be emphasized by a preference for using visual language, such as "let's see" and "my view is..." Visual learning can be highly effective because images are often much more appealing and accessible than words. When you pick up a newspaper, are your eyes instantly drawn to the opening paragraph of a story or the photograph that goes with it?

According to this theory, eyes darting to the side, toward the ears, can reflect a reliance on sound and hearing. Again, someone who responds well to sound may use language that reflects this: "I hear you..." "Sounds like a good idea" and so on. Sound is certainly important to all of us as we learn – the tone of a voice, as well as its modulation and volume, can make a huge difference to how we take in spoken information. Stress on one word rather than another could make all the difference to the message we are receiving from the speaker. Also, a narrative delivered with lively enthusiasm and using the full range of the voice is much more memorable than one spoken in flat, inexpressive tones – the ear as well as the mind must be stimulated to maintain your interest and optimize your learning capacity.

The other senses – taste, touch and smell – also play a vital role in our learning processes. Schools and colleges now place great emphasis on active self-discovery, using the full range of the senses, as opposed to relying on passive reading. Recollection of information or past experiences can often be triggered through a familiar smell or taste rather than words.

Think about how you, as an individual, rely on your senses to learn. What sort of language do you use or respond well to? Perhaps you would like to "chew this over" or the answer may be "on the tip of your tongue". Hopefully, you don't "smell a rat". Being aware of the learning potential that your senses offer can not only intensify your powers of understanding, but give your life another fascinating and enjoyable dimension, too.

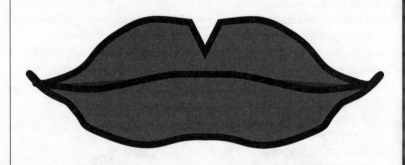

In the final analysis, you alone control your ability and desire to learn. Advice from others is all very well, but unless you make an effort to use it, no one can help you. The tips on learning technique outlined below are largely a matter of common sense, yet many people completely overlook them. Take the plunge and decide to review your current method of learning now – you might discover that you are missing out on all kinds of learning opportunities.

Tips for positive thinking

Your state of mind dictates your ability to learn and succeed. If you tell yourself that you can't do something, the chances are you won't be able to. Instead of imposing these restrictions on yourself, think positive and focus on what you can do.

Try treating your brain as a sophisticated filing cabinet, containing positive and negative files. If you have a problem with numbers, for example, try shifting this mentally from a negative to a positive file. You will find that this can alter all kinds of subconscious preconceptions and totally alter the way you view your skills.

Always stress what you have got right, rather than what went wrong. This encourages a positive outlook and a heightened desire to know more. Everybody makes mistakes, but realizing how much you have learned in order to get as far as you have can boost your confidence and keep you going through the most difficult of situations.

Learn from your mistakes. Dejection is much more likely to set in if your mistakes always prompt feelings of failure rather than providing springboards for further progress. Work through your errors and try to gain something from them – don't give up and start resorting to wild guesses that will teach you nothing.

5 The way in which you deal with the past, present and future is a vital area of learning. Learning is much easier if you try to connect new information with past experience. When trying to remember a date, for instance, associating the numbers with those of a particular birthday or house number may prove invaluable. In this way, fresh information complements your existing store of knowledge rather than becoming a new file in the brain that is inevitably harder to locate.

6 Use visualization techniques to help you take on new information with greater ease. Try imagining yourself standing in the middle of a long road. Your past knowledge stretches away behind you, and the way ahead – your future learning path – is totally uncluttered.

7 The sky's the limit. Success is not limited – you need to recognize that you can never learn too much. The opportunities are always there, just waiting to be grasped.

8 No one else can help you if you don't help yourself. If you're confused about something, say so! Coming clean early on could prevent all kinds of complex problems and embarrassment later on.

9 Take notice of what makes other people succeed. Do you have a real problem with complicated calculations, for example, whereas your colleague manages them with ease? Instead of simply feeling resentful, try and find out how they approach the task. Some people believe that if you go even further and imitate some of the mannerisms and attitudes of that person, you can begin to get under their skin and so excel in the same areas. Your life cannot be a constant act, however – use the experience to question where you are going wrong and to get yourself on the right path.

Reinforcement is sure to improve your powers of retention. This can mean questioning and participation, reading around a certain subject to add to your understanding, reviewing your knowledge at regular intervals, drawing up effective revision plans, and so on. Revision plans should be viewed as a fundamental part of an effective course of learning. When reading, a continual cycle of skimming, questioning, note-taking and recall testing is guaranteed to produce results to be proud of. The more time you spend planting an idea in your head, the harder it will be to uproot it.

Reading and writing are not the only ways to learn and remember. Look and listen carefully to everything around you. Use visual images if you respond well to those – a visual image of a lecturer in action can often trigger information you thought was lost. This does mean, however, that you need to watch and listen carefully to the lecturer in the first place!

Be creative. Play around with ideas by creating poems, sketches, and songs around the subject-matter in question. Nurture your creativity. Because it is so valuable in helping you to stay interested in a subject, it may repay you with interest.

Experiment with music for the mind. While many prefer to study information in silence, some people say that certain types of music actually help them to learn – which type is up to you to discover. You may well find that it helps your concentration as well as increasing your enjoyment of the learning process.

Give yourself a break. If you study from dawn until dusk, your interest will wane, and your learning ability will start to slow down. Try to maintain a balanced lifestyle, and keep your course of learning in perspective. Learn to take regular breaks and vary your environment – try a 5-minute walk around the garden. Constant study may well nourish your conscience, but your mind, like your body, is not programmed for endless exercise, and needs a chance to draw breath every now and again.

15 Establish the learning environment that is best for you. Some people thrive on early morning study, while others cannot even pick up a book until the evening. Experiment a little and discover your best learning environment – the hour, day or place that brings out the best in you. This may also encourage you to feel at ease with the prospect of learning, which is always beneficial.

16 When you can find an interesting or amusing slant to something, you are much more likely to take it in. Making learning stimulating and entertaining helps maximize your motivation and achievement.

17 Feel good about life, your health and learning, and your performance will follow. Look after your body, and your brain will perform much better. You are in the driving seat, and all kinds of learning opportunities are waiting just around the corner. The speed with which you reach them is up to you.

Answers

How Does it Work?

Answers

1.c 2.d 3.d 4.a 5.b
6.c 7.e 8.a 9.b 10.e

Your score

6 or less correct: Poor. Don't be discouraged – this is the kind of skill that can easily be improved.

7 or 8 correct: Good. Having a look at a few alternative learning techniques could improve your performance even more.

9 or 10 correct: Excellent. You have highly tuned talents where learning and recall are concerned. You might still benefit from looking at different learning strategies, however.

Finding The Right Words

Answers

1K. 2E. 3I. 4M. 5C. 6N. 7L. 8B.

Your Score.

4 or below: Needs improvement.

5 or 6 correct: Good.

7 or 8 correct: Excellent.

Maximize Your Memory

An efficient memory can add so much to your life, and yet many people simply say things like, "Oh, don't ask me, I can never remember a thing" and do nothing to make matters better. The following tests will help you to identify your position on the memory scale, pinpointing specific areas for self-improvement.

Use the following questionnaire to get a good general impression of how well your memory performs on a day-to-day basis.

Scoring

Circle the number that you consider to be most appropriate: circle 1 if the statement definitely applies to you; 2 if this is the case sometimes, or you aren't quite sure; 3 if this is never the case.

1. When bumping into a long-lost acquaintance in the street, I can rarely remember his or her name.   1   2   3

2. I tend to forget people's birthdays if I don't have some kind of written reminder.   1   2   3

3. When reading a book, I can quite easily forget what I've just read in the previous chapter.   1   2   3

4. Food shopping without a list often means that I end up having to make extra trips to the store.   1   2   3

5. I have been guilty of forgetting to pass on vital phone messages.   1   2   3

6. I often rely on other people to remind me to do a particular thing.   1   2   3

7. It seems to take me ages to master any new words or foreign phrases.   1   2   3

8. It's unlikely that I would be able to remember a phone number if someone said it to me on the spur of the moment.   **1**   **2**   **3**

9. After being distracted in mid-conversation, I sometimes find myself asking what I was talking about before I was interrupted.   **1**   **2**   **3**

10. When it comes to following instructions for a recipe or a complicated gadget, I need to refer to them even after I've cooked the dish or used the gadget several times.   **1**   **2**   **3**

11. I have a tendency to forget either to watch a specific TV programme or to set the VCR for something I wanted to see.   **1**   **2**   **3**

12. I have burned food before now simply because I forgot it was in the oven.   **1**   **2**   **3**

13. Occasionally, I have waited ages for the kettle to boil and then realized that I have forgotten to switch it on.   **1**   **2**   **3**

14. I sometimes over-sleep when I have failed to set the alarm clock.   **1**   **2**   **3**

15. I have been known to turn up at a class or at work, having left an important document at home.   **1**   **2**   **3**

16. When I have stored something valuable in a "safe" place, it sometimes takes me a long time to hunt it out again.   **1**   **2**   **3**

17. If I'm taking some medicine, there will be times when I find myself wondering whether or not I have actually taken it.   **1**   **2**   **3**

18. I have sometimes totally forgotten to make a vital phone call.   1   2   3

19. I have trouble remembering which key is which when I'm carrying quite a few around with me.   1   2   3

20. I rarely remember what I've spent all my money on.   1   2   3

Number Memory

In a world dominated by advanced telecommunications, and the many numerical codes that go with this, a good memory for numbers can make your life a whole lot easier. Test your short-term number memory by reading each of the following lines of digits aloud once, then turning away to write the numbers down in the same order.

Scoring

For each line, see how many digits in a row you manage to remember correctly before making a mistake. When you get to the longer lines of numbers, see what your average score is (a score of 5 equals 5 numbers in a row remembered correctly).

5

3 1

3 9 4

7 2 8 9

3 1 0 8 6

6 1 8 7 3 1

1 0 4 7 9 2 4

9 8 7 1 4 3 8 9

5 7 9 4 8 9 1 6 0

1 7 8 6 9 7 3 8 7 5

Putting Names to Faces

Have you ever had the uncomfortable experience of bluffing your way through a chance meeting in the street with someone whose identity has completely eluded you? If so, you will know only too well that remembering a visual image is often of little use unless you can put a name to it. See how well you do when trying to remember the names and occupations of the following 12 uniformed people. You have two minutes before covering this box up, turning to the anonymous faces on the right, and seeing if you can give their identities back to them.

Mr Hazlewood, nurse   Ms Stacy, police officer   Ms Dupont, deep-sea diver

Ms Bukowski, firefighter

Mr Bergman, surgeon

Ms Harris, tennis player

Ms O'Riordon, violinist

Ms Brady, mechanic

Mr Rankin, artist

Mr Sorenson, carpenter

Mr Gibson, office worker

Ms Williamsburg, chef

Scoring

Score 2 for each person for whom you gave both the correct name and occupation, 1 if you got either one or the other correct, and 0 if you got neither correct. You will soon discover just how much easier visual images can be to recall than names.

Visual Memory

Images can often be stored away in the memory and recalled much more efficiently than numbers or words. This is particularly true if the images are related in some way. Study these objects, all of which have something to do with the head or face, for 1 minute. Now turn the book over and make a list of the objects you can recall.

> ## I have a photographic memory, but just occasionally I forget to take off the lens cap
>
> (anon – joke)

When you say "Oh dear, I've completely forgotten" about something, you might think that whatever it is you've forgotten is no longer stored in your memory and is lost forever. This is not the case. An inefficient memory is much more likely to be caused by an inability to recall things, rather than a failure to retain the information in the first place.

To take just a couple of examples, have extremely precise details and images from long ago suddenly burst into your consciousness, although they seemed lost for years? Or has a dream ever unexpectedly come to mind? A vast mass of information is locked away in your memory – all you have to do is find the key.

Where does memory come from?

It seems that memory is not exclusively connected with one particular part of the brain. Because of the countless links between the huge numbers of brain cells, memory processes are constantly taking place all over this remarkable organ. More specific types of memory are, however, thought to spring from specific regions of the brain. An area called the limbic system, for example, is thought to have strong links with the way in which we record and recall general impressions. This is also the region that controls raw emotion, sex drive and appetite. Short-term memory, which lasts up to about 30 seconds, appears to be controlled by the temporal lobes on each side of the brain, while the parietal lobes behind the ears seem to be responsible for retaining knowledge of simple tasks. Visual memory occurs in the occipital lobes at the rear of the brain.

What this means is that serious damage to any of these regions of the brain can have severe consequences for the memory. In one case, a man whose temporal lobes had been badly damaged by an accident was left unable to recall the details of any recent events. Keeping up with the plot of a movie or simply knowing where he had been just a few hours previously became impossible tasks. So next time you complain about how poor your memory is, think again!

A question of age

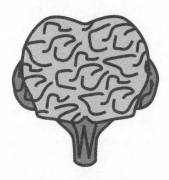

Age is directly related to memory skills, so there is little point in comparing the memory of a nine- and a ninety-year-old. For example, as young children, our frontal lobes, which are linked to the way we use language, are not yet fully developed. This means that a child's ability to distinguish between fact and fiction and to remember things accurately is also under-developed. How many times must this have been at the root of arguments between siblings, each convinced of their own version of a family saga? Just talking about things often helps to clear up some of these kinds of discrepancies, because verbal stimulation can trigger all kinds of memories.

At the other end of the scale, memory is said to deteriorate with age. But if you consider how many more memories seventy-year-olds have to contend with compared to their young grandchildren, it's hardly surprising that a few fall by the wayside! This may well be the result of a "last-in, first-out" principle: with new information constantly overlapping old, early memories are frequently the memorable. It's easy enough to recall the last meal you ate, but could you remember what you had for lunch exactly a month ago today?

There is encouraging evidence that older people today have far more efficient memories than their counterparts in previous generations. The sheer potential of the memory has been hugely underestimated in the past – now each year brings new scientific insights into the workings of the brain and memory, and there seems to be no limit to what can be achieved.

Remembering ... and forgetting

Apart from age, there are many other factors that affect memory – not least of which is information overload. The continual barrage of new information that many of us face every day will inevitably affect the amount of knowledge to which we have instant access. Learning something fresh is never easy when your head is full of all kinds of other information. What is needed to overcome this problem is an organized, firmly focused mind.

Remembering is not the sole function of an efficient memory – much of what we "forget" also plays a vital role in our lives. If we were able to recall every single piece of trivia, from the exact dialogue of every conversation we have ever had to the precise ingredients of every meal we have eaten, then locating important bits of information would be a superhuman task. The extremely selective nature of the memory not only smooths our path in life, but it also interprets the past in a manner that fits in with our desires. This "editing" effect has both good and bad consequences. On one hand, it means that unpleasant memories can be wiped, which may often be a good thing. On the other hand, it means that events can be grossly distorted. This is why it is essential to talk about shared memories with other people, in order to stay as objective as possible.

Giving yourself a prompt

Just as conversation can cause memories to come flooding back, so can
specific circumstances or events, whether these are related to sight, smell
or sound. Forgotten details can often be unlocked by making a return visit
to a relevant environment. Obviously, if you want to jolt memories of a
trip around the world, this method might not be feasible, but if you left
your keys somewhere while out shopping, retracing your steps may prove
invaluable.

As we've already mentioned in the learning chapter, it may be that the eyes
play an important role in revealing how we recall events. Some research
suggests that people's eyes immediately dart upward, downward, to the left
or to the right when asked to recall matters that they connect strongly with
their hearing, sight or touch. Darting in one particular direction could mean
that the memories in question relate to a specific sense – looking sideways,
towards the ears, for example, may indicate the auditory sense. Like the
different ways of learning that we've already looked at, an efficient memory
often stems from making full use of all of the senses.

The three major ways of learning and remembering are:

REPETITION

ASSOCIATION

VISUALIZATION

Repeating Yourself Yourself Yourself

Simple repetition is not always enough for really effective learning and recollection, and repeating things over and over is not calculated to fill most people with enthusiasm. Repetition tends to produce effective recall only where simpler tasks are concerned. For more complex ones, properly organized memorizing is needed. Various techniques can be used. For example, the ability to recall written information is helped greatly by note-taking and by regular reviews – after half an hour, a day, a month.

The Art of Association

When it comes to everyday life, and the need to remember a friend's phone number or what to buy at the supermarket, it's time to turn to a more approachable method – mnemonics. Mnemonics are simple, effective tricks to improve your memory, while stimulating your creativity at the same time. Repeating a phone number in your head because you don't have a pen with you could serve you well until you get home and write it down, but what are your chances of recalling the same number a week or month later without any other aid? Instead, try the following mnemonic method. Form a sentence by picking a word to represent each digit. The word should have the same number of letters as the digit it represents. For example:

The number **346443** could be remembered as

"all (3 letters) good (4) things (6) take (4) time (4) too (3)."

Try remembering the reference number B437 FEM, a mix of numbers and letters, with:

"Bedraggled (B) ants (4) ate (3) eagerly (7) for (F) eight (E) minutes (M)."

This method of association is easy to master – the more you do it, the easier it becomes. You will also find it an entertaining way of expanding your creative skills.

Using your visualizing skills

Images are also excellent memory aids. A written diary could become a thing of the past if more people developed the various tried and tested visual mnemonic techniques. Try remembering specific objects or events by placing them within a familiar visual context. For example, you might need to remember to find out about booking a trip abroad. Now imagine a walk through a very familiar place – your home or the local park, for example. As you go, insert images of relevant items – a wallet might remind you to work out how much foreign currency you need for your trip.

This method is an excellent one for remembering a list of objects or a sequence of events – from a shopping list to the step-by-step procedure for converting one program to another on your computer. You could try making the first thing that you pass on your route the most important item or event. Or perhaps the order of the images might mirror the chronological order of the events you are trying to memorize. In this way, the schedule for your week ahead might be committed to memory by a mental walk around your garden. Visualize a computer sinking beneath the waters of your pond (finish that vital report); a casket overflowing with coins under the oak tree (chase up unpaid invoices); a huge conductor's baton in the vegetable patch with tomato plants growing up it (a concert outing one evening), and so on...

The surroundings should remain unchanged, only the images you have inserted in order to remind you of something must be new. Ideally, the same scene with the same route should be used for every list you ever want to keep in your mind – with frequent use, remembering lists will become automatic.

If you make the added items and their position within your scenario obscure, out of place or amusing, they will linger in your memory much longer. The image of a giant fish, wearing sunglasses and relaxing happily in your bath, would make you much more likely to remember to buy that fish tank!

Playing the system

You can begin to see just how effective systematic memory methods can be. Look at the letter triangle below. Read it through as if it were normal text, then cover it up and try to reproduce it yourself.

```
S
T  N
A  H  P
E  L  E  Y
T  N  I  A  D
```

Rather than storing information in countless single pieces, and laboriously fighting through them all in search of what you need, storing chunks of information enables quicker, more efficient access. Remembering two words is far easier than recalling 15 separate and seemingly random letters. Just as documents can be rapidly retrieved from a filing cabinet divided into a logical sequence of ordered sections, so information be recalled more easily from a well-structured memory. Of course one person will use a different filing system to another – test yourself to discover what works best for you.

Recalling written material

Being able to retain and recall text is a vital skill for school, college, work and hobbies. Yet most people fail to organize the way in which they read and run the risk of losing up to 80% of the information after just 24 hours. So resolve to follow the BARCS system next time you want to be able to recall something you are reading:

Breaks:

Have frequent short breaks between intensive periods of study, preferably after 45 minutes to an hour. Try to break for about 15 mins if you can, but any break is better than none. View this as a necessity, not an indulgence.

Activity:

The memory performs much more efficiently if you approach reading actively. Take notes, read aloud, walk around the garden with the text – anything to help focus your attention.

Reviews:

Review your previous learning session after each break – just take a couple of minutes to note down what you can remember.

Comparisons:

Compare your notes with the original text. Any errors or omissions will be drilled further into your memory.

Strengthen:

Spend a few minutes reinforcing the summarized material – a day later, a week later and a month later. You should find that much of this information will stay at your fingertips for a long time.

Your reading skills are closely intertwined with your powers of retention. If you learn to retain things more efficiently, you will find yourself reading faster, and focusing your attention more intensely. And time may be of the essence – for a student, less time spent reading means more time for valuable revision. Reading skills are examined in more depth later on (see pages 40–54).

Pay Attention, But Enjoy Yourself Too

Failure to remember things cannot simply be attributed to a poor memory. Recollection may be impossible because the information simply wasn't absorbed and retained in the first place. Fundamental to an efficient memory is the ability to pay attention – if your mind wanders off to distant places while you are being told how to use a new computer, how can you even expect to remember how to turn the machine on?

Learn to concentrate on important details. When meeting new business clients, repeat their names over and over silently to yourself, making a mental note of any helpful associations. You might meet a Ms Redland, and remember her name because she has quite a reddish, ruddy complexion. Distinctive characteristics serve as great memory aids – as ever, the sillier, the better!

Improving your memory can be fun, and you can achieve astonishingly impressive results very quickly. Party games demanding the rapid memorizing of a tray of objects is quite literally child's play – making up a story that links the apparently unconnected items lodges them firmly in the memory. Some people can "magically" memorize the exact order of an entire pack of playing cards. The method, however, is simple: give the cards identities that you can then link up in the correct sequence. Perhaps you might like to remember each card as a member of a couple of sports teams, for example. Again, it's simply a matter of bundling together disparate images to form a collective group.

Rhymes can also prove to be highly entertaining memory-joggers. Just think of the children's rhymes that you sang years ago, yet can still remember. You could well find that your rhyming experiments render written lists unnecessary. Either compose your own little ditties, full of relevant references, or use a predetermined list of significant words. For this, try assigning a word to each letter of your name. If your name was Jane, this might be jumper for J, apple for A, and so on. Now try to connect each item on the list to each of these words in some way and create your rhyme. You can have a lot of fun making up really bizarre rhymes, but you will need to imprint jumper, apple etc on your memory – remember to remember!

The Role of Your Subconscious

Your subconscious plays a huge role in influencing what you can and cannot remember. Anything your mind connects with fear and unease is guaranteed to impair performance – it's highly likely that at least once in your life you have emerged from a long-dreaded examination of some sort feeling really stupid because you forgot a basic fact or theory. Try to spend time relaxing and preparing yourself mentally for any stressful situations that require a healthily functioning memory. Pinpointing the cause of your fear should enable you to tackle it positively and leave your memory free of unnecessary hindrances. Adequate preparation will help to ensure that any fear is minimized, and your performance maximized.

As with everything, practice makes perfect – your memory will not improve unless you work at it. Shopping lists may serve as a reminder when you get to the supermarket, but you must remember to take the list along in the first place! The memory tips outlined in this section will become second nature if you make a little time to tackle them properly. You will then be able to trust your memory as much as it deserves. People often say, rightly, that the brain is far more intricate than any computer, so, unless you use and service it regularly, you can never get the most from it.

See For Yourself

Assuming that you have remembered what you have just read, your memory should already be able to put into practice some of what it has learned. Tackling the tests below will show you how straightforward the memory techniques outlined above really are, while giving you an opportunity to devise simple methods of your own. The omission of a scoring system here is deliberate – you have already established how effective your basic memory skills are.

This is only the start of a promising future for your memory. Soon, your improved performance will say it all.

Spot the Difference

Try tackling this game of spot the difference. Cover the pictureabove, and study the picture below for no more than 1 minute, trying to absorb every detail. Now cover the picture below and look at the slightly different version of the picture above. What are the differences? There is no time limit, but your short-term memory deteriorates with time so the differences are unlikely to seem so obvious after a minute or two.

Memorizing a List – Against the Clock

Now imagine that you've discovered an antique trunk full of all kinds of objects, in the depths of a wild forest. It has obviously been hidden there, undiscovered, for decades. You suddenly notice that, in your excitement, you have lagged far behind your companions, and desperately try to memorize the collection so that you can relate what you saw when you finally catch up. You know that you only have a couple of minutes to spare, or you will lose your friends completely, so concentrate, and see what you can remember after the five minutes that it will take you to rejoin your crowd.

Number-crunching

Spend two minutes studying the table of numbers below before covering it up and trying to reproduce it yourself. Remember that simple repetition techniques may not be sufficient
to help you.

2	6	6	1
3	4	2	6
6	3	6	0
4	2	1	8

Answers

Self-assessment quiz

Your score:

20-33 Your memory seems to be letting you down, and could well benefit from some of the advice offered later on. For example, try using written reminders as a back-up aid. Perhaps it is actually your lifestyle that is to blame. Your life may be so hectic that you are simply placing too much strain on your poor old memory.

34-47 You appear to have a fairly reliable memory, with the occasional lapse from time to time. Learning a few useful techniques will help to heighten your memory skills further, especially when it comes to remembering things with greater accuracy.

48-60 Congratulations – your memory is in pretty good shape. You seldom forget things, perhaps largely as a result of a well-organized lifestyle. Read on to identify any more specific deficiencies, and to find out how you can improve your memory power even further.

Number Memory

Your score (for the longer number lines)

1-4 Poor. Although you are below average now, however, there is plenty you can do to raise your scores.

5-7 Average. Your number memory is very much like most people's – which means that there's room for a little improvement.

8-10 Outstanding. Your short-term numerical memory serves you very well. Perhaps it's time to look at other areas of your memory skills, such as your visual memory.

Visual Memory

Objects connected with the head and face

Your score:

1-7 Poor. The memory aids detailed later on will point you in the right direction.

8-10 Average. Your visual memory is pretty efficient, but you can still benefit from further practice.

11-12 Outstanding. Your visual memory is a major asset.

Playing the System

It is unlikely that you met with much success. But careful study reveals that the words "dainty elephants" are trapped in the triangle as you read right to left, starting from the bottom right. Reproducing the letter triangle now is no problem.

Memorizing a list – against the clock

Possible memorizing methods include the mnemonic system of moving through a scene; use of rhyme, although time is limited; and attaching words or images to the items.

Number Crunching

Suggested memorizing method: the diagonals read 2, 4, 6, 8 and 1, 2, 3, 4; there is a double 6 in the top row and a 6 on either side. Now just fill in the gaps so that each column adds up to 15.

Putting Names to Faces

Your score

0-13 Poor. You need to work through a few memory tips and techniques in order to exploit your potential.

14-20 Good. Keep working on your memory skills to improve even further.

21-24 Excellent. Your memory seems to cope pretty well with the tricky combination of word lists and visual images.

Spot the Difference

1. Swimming costume on child was striped in left picture, but spotty in right

2. Bucket is missing

3. Mum's sunglasses have been removed

4. One less boat is visible on the water

5. The windsurfer has no board

6. Part of the sandcastle is missing

7   The prominent cloud on the left is a different shape

8   The pattern on the beach-towel has changed

9   The fair-haired child now has dark hair

10 Dad was sitting on deckchair; he is now sitting on a sun-lounger

11 The waves are now capped with white foam

12 The vehicle pulled up at the back of the beach is different in right picture

You may not find it useful to apply any particular method here – instead, try focusing your attention by describing the images out loud or connecting individual features with past experience or even certain words. Hopefully, you will feel that your visual memory has a new heightened awareness.

Reading Skills

Without basic literacy, everyday life can turn into a series of insurmountable hurdles. Having a strong command of language and reading skills unlocks the gate to a much more stimulating and rewarding world. Read on to see how you fare.

Test Your Wordpower

Find the definitions that most closely correspond to the following words.

polemic
- a. having electric charges
- b. extreme cold
- c. controversial
- d. at a height

fardel
- a. agricultural tool
- b. burden
- c. remote place
- d. obese

objurgate
- a. reprimand
- b. cancel
- c. replace
- d. urge

extemporaneous
- a. done without preparation
- b. at the same time as
- c. temporary
- d. done in advance

5 pilose
- a. criminal activity
- b. drug addiction
- c. covered with hair
- d. cheerful

6 juvenescence
- a. period of study
- b. composition
- c. state of complete elation
- d. immaturity

7 voluble
- a. talkative
- b. gullible
- c. generous
- d. overflowing

8 julep
- a. member of the mint family
- b. type of drink
- c. encouragement
- d. children's game

9 anneal

a. heat metal or glass to toughen it
b. treat wound
c. apply protective covering
d. make member of a royal order

10 oleaginous

a. prehistoric
b. shiny
c. deceitful
d. oily or greasy

11 lustrate

a. add extra diagrams
b. perform ritual purification
c. robust fitness
d. enthuse

12 unguent

a. stilted and hesitant
b. ointment
c. African hunter
d. strong adhesive

13 brio

a. rivalry
b. the "spirit of the age"
c. verve and vivacity
d. arrogance

14 cabochon

a. rank in the French army
b. type of wheel common in ceremonial carriages
c. polished gem without facets
d. clever trick

15 cicerone

a. person lacking courage
b. conductor of sightseers
c. heat-loving insect
d. ancient temple

16 rondo

a. piece of music
b. Italian pasta dish
c. lively dance
d. poem of 10 or 13 lines

7 tamarin

   a. evergreen tree
   b. musical instrument
   c. tropical fruit
   d. South American monkey

8 mettle

   a. conductor of heat
   b. courage
   c. interfere
   d. weld together

19 sibilant

   a. with a hissing sound
   b. close family relation
   c. family reunion
   d. ecstasy

20 eclogue

   a. environmental study
   b. short poem
   c. position of the moon
   d. general discussion

Playing the Detective

Your task here is to find the intruder among the following groups of words.

1
a. skivvy
b. servant
c. slave
d. factotum
e. employer

2
a. independence
b. freedom
c. coercion
d. liberty
e. licence

3
a. deviate
b. digress
c. branch out
d. decelerate
e. divaricate

4
a. initiate
b. procrastinate
c. delay
d. put off
e. postpone

5
a. vigilance
b. observation
c. watchfulness
d. inertia
e. invigilation

6
a. curiosity
b. zeal
c. nonchalance
d. officiousness
e. interest

7
a. enormous
b. infinitesimal
c. gigantic
d. capacious
e. immense

8
a. cornea
b. indigestion
c. nausea
d. anaemia
e. meningitis

212

a. depict
b. illustrate
c. draw
d. resent
e. sketch

a. versatility
b. ambidextrousness
c. flexibility
d. adaptability
e. conductibility

a. lingo
b. dialect
c. idiom
d. parlance
e. auditory

a. insatiable
b. gluttonous
c. vivacious
d. devouring
e. voracious

Speed Reading

Studies have shown that faster reading enhances learning and memory skills, as well as having the obvious benefit of saving time. Use the following passage to test your reading skills. All you need are a watch with a second hand to time yourself and a pen to record your starting and finishing times. Take care to read as you would normally – the aim here is to test your current ability, enabling you to determine how far you need to improve.

After timing your reading of the passage, tackle the multiple-choice comprehension test. Do this without referring to the passage at all, selecting the statement that most closely corresponds to the text.

The Text

Eugène Boudin (1824-1898) is renowned for the many beach scenes he painted at Trouville, on the coast of Normandy in France. Coastal themes dominated his prolific output, which included almost 4,000 oil paintings. Having had a childhood strongly influenced by the sea, this lifelong artistic interest comes as little surprise.

He was born at Honfleur, a seaside town where Eugène's father Leonard had followed the tradition of countless Honfleur men before him by becoming a sailor. Leonard Boudin began his apprenticeship for the navy at the tender age of 11, later acting as a gunner in battles on the high seas against the English. He then swapped his bullets for a fishing rod, and began to earn a living fishing for cod. After eight years of marriage, Louis-Eugène was born on the 12th of July, 1824.

Early Promise

Leonard Boudin's many years at sea enabled him to take charge of a small vessel trading between Rouen and Honfleur. His talented son was soon on board working as a cabin boy, and passed the time during breaks from his tasks by sketching. Even from a young age, Eugène Boudin was uplifted and inspired by life on the water.

Following a move to Le Havre in 1835, where his father took up a new shipping job, Eugène began to attend a school run by priests. Here, his artistic talents flourished. At the age of 12, however, this came to an abrupt end when Leonard decided to curtail his son's education and the boy began work as a printer's clerk in Le Havre. He then moved on to a job in a stationer's, where he worked his way up and became the owner's secretary. Despite offering little prospect of further promotion, Eugène received a gift from the owner of this stationer's that would have a vital influence on him: his first paintbox.

A New Era Dawns

In 1838, the development of steamship traffic at this time enabled Leonard to find work on a steamer called Le Français, which frequented Honfleur and Le Havre.

Eugène's mother also took to the seas, working as a stewardess on steamships in the area. Yet neither his parents' occupations, nor his early experience on the ocean, stimulated any desire in Eugène to follow a similar path. Instead, he formed a partnership with a foreman who had also worked for Lemasle, the stationers at which Eugène had previously been employed. This partnership gave birth to a new stationer's shop, and allowed Eugène to enjoy the work of visiting artists whose pictures they framed and displayed.

The personal contact that Boudin maintained with these artists and their work made him determined to become a painter himself. Despite words of warning offered by the artist Jean-François Millet about the precariousness of such a profession, Boudin carried on regardless. After arguing with his partner Jean Archer, in 1846, Boudin left their shop to embark on a life devoted to the art he loved. It was this powerful devotion alone that would keep him going through the difficult years that lay ahead.

The Lure of the Sea

The hypnotic magic of the open water came to rule Boudin's otherwise miserable struggle to survive, and he often worked in the open air, overlooking the sea. Extremely modest sales of his work were enough to fuel his passion for painting, and his passion to learn more about the great masters.

Le Havre's offerings were limited – what Boudin needed to quench his thirst for knowledge was Paris, with its museums and stimulating artistic life. A year after ending his partnership, Boudin's scrimping and saving paid off and he arrived in Paris. What awaited him was not the land of his dreams – survival in the city was, in many ways, more of a struggle than the provincial life that he was accustomed to. Boudin did, however, spend endless hours studying the paintings he so revered, which taught him a great deal but also filled him with despair at what he saw as his own inadequacy. This despondency would remain with him throughout his artistic life.

Any travel was a large undertaking for a man so attached to his native land. Boudin's trip around Belgium and northern France was purely the result of a certain Baron Taylor, whose interest in art led him to run several societies that helped aspiring artists who needed financial support. This support helped all of the parties concerned: while Boudin toured around displaying his work, he sold lottery tickets in aid of artists in a similar situation to himself.

Comprehension

1.
a. Boudin produced 4,000 pieces of work.
b. Boudin created just under 4,000 paintings on a coastal theme.
c. His total output included almost 4,000 oil paintings.

2.
a. Before departing for Paris, Boudin enjoyed an extravagant lifestyle.
b. Boudin saved for a considerable time before leaving for Paris.
c. A grant funded Boudin's first trip to Paris.

3.
a. Eugène Boudin's first job was at sea.
b. Eugène Boudin trained as a gunner.
c. Eugène Boudin started work when he was 12 years old.

4.
a. Lemasle provided Eugène with his first set of paints.
b. Eugène's father was responsible for his first encounter with the world of painting.
c. Eugène was given his first box of paints while at a school run by priests.

5.
a. Boudin's first exhibition took place in Paris.
b. The first significant exhibition of Boudin's paintings was in Le Havre.
c. Boudin never had a proper display of his work.

6.
a. Leonard Boudin worked on the first steamship.
b. Leonard Boudin found work during the rise in the use of steamships.
c. Leonard Boudin helped develop the use of steamships.

7.
a. Eugène was always confident about his work.
b. Eugène continually criticized his own work.
c. Eugène became known as an art critic.

8.
a. Much of Eugène's work stemmed from his study of the sea.
b. As a young man, Eugène dreamed of a career on the waves.
c. Eugène preferred to work indoors.

9.
a. Baron Taylor purchased Eugène's early still lifes.
b. Eugène's three-year stay in Paris was financed by Baron Taylor.
c. Eugène was commissioned by the Baron to make copies of works by the great masters.

10.
a. Eugène's father emulated many previous Honfleur seamen.
b. Eugène was born in Le Havre.
c. Eugène was born in Trouville.

An estimated 40% of adults across the world are said to be unable to read. Reading is not just a question of making a concentrated effort to recognize a series of visual symbols. It also becomes an integral part of the way we process information, enabling us to read words quicker than we could say them – we've all had the experience of the eyes being swifter than the tongue.

In Control

In general terms, the processing of language is controlled by the left half of the brain. Within this half, specific regions are responsible for different types of language manipulation. Being able to write, and the ability to control your voice, stems from processes that take place in the frontal lobe. Damage to the parietal lobe, toward the back of the brain, can result in alexia, a condition where it becomes difficult to read words without confusing the letters. The temporal lobe, located by the ear, and the outer layer of the parietal lobe, control the capacity to understand what it being said to us. Harming these areas can result in deafness – if this happens to a child, learning to read can be an upward struggle.

The Process of Reading

We all appreciate that efficient reading skills can extend our understanding and vocabulary, while a poor reading technique and selection of reading matter can substantially hinder our progress. Focusing exclusively on reading as rapidly as possible often results in a failure to grasp the meaning of the material, and the reader may need to begin all over again. The ideal reading technique involves the use of careful, considered skimming strategies. For example, an initial scan of a piece of text gives the reader a broad overview, enabling the brain to focus properly on the general subject matter. Just as the body needs warming up before vigorous exercise, so too does the mind.

The Eyes Have It

Different reading techniques are often linked to eye movement. Studies have shown how reading requires a continual, rapid cycle of stops and starts, the eyes focusing suddenly on a batch of letters before swooping on to the next batch. Due to the brain's preference for chunks of information, as opposed to single bits, the more words that can be absorbed at a glance, the easier and quicker it is to learn.

The overview obtained by effective skimming can make a huge difference to your powers of comprehension and recall. There is no specific scanning method – the eyes may wander vertically, horizontally and diagonally across the page, focusing on individual key words, phrases and titles. A page may be scanned in anything from 2 to 20 seconds. The speed and technique is unique to each individual, as are the resulting benefits.

Perhaps most importantly, skimming can lessen the fear that many people feel when reading something new. Escaping the feeling that you must concentrate equally on every word helps to set the mind at ease. The more relaxed reading that will follow on from this makes the entire process altogether more rewarding.

Flexibility is the Key

Whatever your reading speed, a good reader needs to maintain a flexible approach. Obviously, a complicated passage requires greater study, with slower reading and less text skimmed or skipped. It has been shown that fast readers may study at a pace similar to slower workers in such sections, but more efficient reading and scanning of less important passages enables their overall speed to be maintained.

The major key to efficient retention and recall of written information is understanding, not merely being able to repeat something "parrot-fashion." If you have a high level of understanding, the brain stays sharply focused on the subject matter and you will find it far easier to read quickly. The foundation stones of effective understanding and efficient reading technique are:

○ The ability to relate individual words and sentences to the context as a whole

○ Maintaining and focusing your interest by taking breaks, making notes, perhaps referring to other texts, making more heavy-going material accessible by linking it with other subjects that you enjoy more

○ Keeping fresh by pausing every so often

Reading can provide us with a whole world of fascinating education and enjoyment – but only if you learn to read actively, with a questioning mind, using it as a springboard for finding out even more.

There are all kinds of easy ways in which you can improve your reading skills.

Making the Most of Your Daily Read

Newspapers provide an invaluable source of reading material, often helping us to improve both our vocabulary range and our speed reading skills. Delving into a range of different newspapers can make us more aware of the different styles of language that are effective in different situations, as well as providing interest and variety. Scanning through a paper helps you to locate articles of immediate interest, improving your ability to focus on what is strictly relevant, and discarding what isn't.

Increasing Your Speeds

Now that you have a general notion of your reading speed, you can formulate a plan of self-improvement. For example, try selecting an article of approximately 1,000 words. Time how long it takes you to read this, and then write a brief summary of the piece to test your overall comprehension. Try to assess yourself as honestly as possible, or you will gain little from the exercise. Find your reading speed per minute by following the process explained on page 43: count the number of words in the article, multiply it by 60, and divide this by your time in seconds. A reasonable amount of practice should result in an increased speed of around 100.

Test Your Scanning Abilities

The exercise overleaf is designed to test your ability to scan a page for the most important information, giving you greater understanding and improved reading efficiency. Your task is to work through each line, glancing at the first group of letters, then marking the position of its twin, positioned somewhere else in each line. As you work through, the letter groups get larger. A metronome may help you to maintain speed – set the pace to correspond with the time it takes you to get through one of the first lines. Trying to stick to this rhythm as you progress will help you to broaden the range of characters your eyes can take in within a given time.

BA	GU	B C	ST	IN	LK	BA	AA
OJ	LP	TG	BC	SE	OJ	QJ	BR
CT	IP	CT	EY	KB	FG	TH	NO
LF	YU	BU	LF	UB	DY	IH	BK
VT	VT	KI	CT	IU	PV	EJ	OG
UI	HD	TB	LK	OG	CR	UM	UI
DE	YU	JU	KI	DE	SG	KU	OL
MO	DT	MO	RT	UH	MV	DE	YG
CX	TE	JH	JI	CX	KT	CT	EC
OT	GY	UI	BF	TD	OT	NU	OP
CV	GT	CV	JY	IJ	OM	LP	DW
KP	HU	TE	PK	KP	RT	VD	IN
CT	ES	WI	UN	HO	PL	BC	CT
BY	UI	JN	BY	ER	OJ	LN	CT
VY	IO	FT	PO	JH	CT	WS	VY
UO	TF	ER	VT	DY	UO	KH	DT
PO	PN	UT	FY	IN	PO	HY	ER
NU	TY	MI	OP	MV	FT	ED	NU
BU	TI	OP	MI	YU	BU	DT	BY
VY	ER	VY	UO	JO	PL	MU	YU
BYT	CRU	OPK	BNT	UIO	TYD	BYT	UIM
VHI	FTY	VSR	EDI	KOM	VHI	DTW	QAU
MOL	BYR	MOL	PHI	TBD	YUI	NOF	GHI
WXT	GUE	WAI	HUB	WXT	UBI	MOP	HIM
EUT	IUY	EUT	GON	BIE	EUF	YBI	UIO
BJD	YRU	DFG	IOU	NUI	VHT	DRT	BJD
LPB	UTD	CTS	HIM	LPB	CTE	UGM	NIT
NIB	HUI	DTE	CUG	NIB	PKT	DEA	JIB
YTE	MIT	UI	HFR	YTE	CFT	LOP	YUI
VTY	UIO	VTY	RSE	YTU	HJI	NPO	MIG
CTY	UIO	JNR	ERT	VJU	CSE	RTF	CTY
IOH	CTE	UIV	SJW	TFA	IOH	OPB	CRA
GYM	KOI	VZE	GYM	VUS	WQA	VRI	OPL
NID	RYG	NIA	WQE	RCG	IOM	NID	PLF
VUE	KOP	LFE	ZPO	VUE	ASU	REL	BUI
NZE	RTY	IGS	BOP	LMV	STQ	UOI	NZE
QRT	UYF	BHU	PAS	LGR	WQD	QRT	UIV
BDT	GUA	BDT	OPG	UTW	DFC	BZH	JUO
CAR	CAR	TYU	CGQ	IGS	PLN	ETU	CAT
MKE	UTV	HSM	MKI	VHA	TEC	MKE	IUB

MAOW	VYSE	YYJV	MAOW	UYRV	MOPD	GTEH	NIPL
BIDT	FTEY	NUIO	MODE	UYIB	BIDT	YUIN	MPLY
SDWR	YUIO	JCEN	NJOM	NSTR	KOPB	MODT	SDWR
MPLD	UITB	XDRW	YUIB	MKOR	YUIJ	MPLD	REWY
CSTW	ITHB	VGIR	CSTW	HJIM	MPLH	UIOD	ETUB
NUOM	JHGD	RYUV	NUIE	NUOM	KPLG	TYIC	EYYC
BUET	HUIP	BUET	DEAU	IJFO	MIFT	ECSU	INFT
MPLG	YRWE	BHIP	MOPD	RTUO	MPLG	YUID	RTUV
BUTE	IOHN	TETY	BUTE	TYIF	JKKR	RTUV	NOIY
VDTE	TYUB	NIOF	TYIU	NOPF	VDTE	TYIB	MIOO
NDAN	RTIJ	BHIL	PFTW	RUVJ	NDAN	KOPL	NCTT
OPLM	TPKG	AHUI	OPLM	VTSR	TYUO	MOJU	FTUO
BHDQ	YIIB	GIUM	VYUO	BUSE	YUON	BHDQ	OKMG
PCZE	TUOB	CJOR	OMVB	TDEY	PCZE	IONF	WRUJ
FALK	IOGD	GTAF	UFAK	LUIU	FALK	OPHC	EOHF
VHIF	GYTI	BHRE	OIHF	JTEF	LKUH	VHIF	IOKH
HDEI	OPKV	DSHE	TUIB	HDEI	OPLM	VSIH	KYVL
UPAI	UPAI	MKOF	EROB	CTSR	YIOJ	BAGU	OMAK
LJST	YIHB	LJST	HUOO	NCTW	TYIB	MKSY	OPNC
BAJI	YUOK	BGST	UPKN	BAJI	PLBD	TUOB	GHAJ

CEWIQ	OPKLC	CEWIQ	LNVK	STUMD	VUSWD	TRUGF	BIDMF
MSIFO	VGJOD	JBHUS	TYUKH	GHHTR	MSIFO	FGHJT	DRFUI
AVGHJ	TINBM	FTUUY	GHUIO	AVGHJ	OPOLM	GYUIU	VTYEJ
BUDTE	BHILJ	VBHYR	HIUJN	KLIPO	VHGUR	HJIOM	BUDTE
VHUIO	KOOPJ	DFTTR	NKOLK	VHUIO	PLVGY	RTJIO	CGHJK
ADFTT	UOIJK	MLKOI	ADFTT	UOINV	GYIOK	BHJTR	IOONF
KGUYR	HGUIM	GHJUY	TYTFJ	IOIHH	RTUYB	KGUYR	BVHUT
FAJDE	TYIKM	VHJKM	RTIOC	FAJDE	YIUON	FKJYM	FHTHM
LVGSD	YUIHV	KIOUI	FTIUB	LPFES	LVGSD	YIOKG	RTIJF
AMOPH	GHUII	NJAIU	YUIOK	AMOPH	DRQWT	PIREV	NJIUT
SGUAI	YGERI	OPJHF	SGUAI	PLMGR	UIOMF	BTGYO	BHTJM
NAGSH	KOLIU	HJSKA	HJIUY	IOIMN	NAGSH	UOJMN	GHJAY
LSNXH	YUIOS	BNJSY	KYIAO	BHJSU	LSNXH	UIAOM	SGETQ
ANSHR	TYAIO	NBSFT	TAIJN	ANSHR	UIOSK	BBBSG	JAJYS
OITFS	HTYEW	RYUOA	OGABS	HSYRS	OITFS	NHGSK	OPPAN
ERLAE	HSOAM	HGSYK	ERLAE	JOPMF	PAFST	YUIOS	BAHJO
SJDHF	SJDHF	UIOPK	SKYRE	JIOMG	FAVHJ	KLPO0	BFSTY
LANSH	JIOIT	GTYJN	KOOGR	LANSH	UIOPK	BFRTY	NGHOK
IWTQY	MAHST	JHQHG	IWTQY	IOISH	NMAJS	NNSJS	USIOA
JSHWW	JSHWW	YYIOP	JLFSW	QDTUO	NFSTT	YUIOK	GSFSK

You can devise similar tests yourself, using letters, numbers or other symbols. Alternatively, try skimming text for a particular (common) word. A conscious effort to read faster and skim better will inevitably improve your skills without a huge amount of effort.

Stretch Your Wordpower

To extend your vocabulary, you will find numerous written tests similar to those in the self-assessment section in other books of this nature. However, the general context of the word is often missing in such tests. Wider reading of a challenging nature, exploiting the full range of books, magazines and newspapers, will help you to develop a more accurate and varied vocabulary.

When writing, having a thesaurus and dictionary to hand provides instant access to a language goldmine. Spelling difficulties can be lessened by examining the word visually – letting your mind absorb the shape, size and quantity of letters. Play around with the word mentally, creating its own identity in your mind. Stimulating the mind in these ways will also help to unlock all kinds of words that you had forgotten you even knew!

Knowledge of some common Latin, Greek and English prefixes and suffixes is always helpful when you don't have a dictionary to hand, because it allows you to make informed guesses about word meanings. A brief list follows.

Prefix stem and example	Definition of prefix	Suffix stem and example	Definition of suffix
<u>ab</u>-stract	away from	enjoy-<u>able</u>	capable of
<u>ad</u>-jacent	next to/towards	cardi-<u>ac</u>	pertaining to
<u>an</u>-aphrodisiac	not/without	advant-<u>age</u>	action/locality
<u>ante</u>-date	before	annu-<u>al</u>	pertaining to
<u>anti</u>-freeze	opposing/against	abund-<u>ance</u>	state/action
<u>arch</u>-angel	principal	pleas-<u>ant</u>	causing/performing action
<u>auto</u>-biography	self	secret-<u>ary</u>	dealing with/
<u>bene</u>-volent	well		place for
<u>bi</u>-focal	twice	anim-<u>ate</u>	cause to be
<u>bio</u>-logy	life	arti-<u>cle</u>	indicating smallness
<u>cent</u>-enary	one hundred	wis-<u>dom</u>	power/condition
<u>centi</u>-grade	one hundreth	wax-<u>en</u>	made of
<u>circum</u>-ference	around	kitt-<u>en</u>	small
<u>com</u>-pose	together/with	acqu-<u>eous</u>	pertaining to
<u>con</u>-tain	together/with	sing-<u>er</u>	belonging to
<u>contra</u>-vene	against	conval-<u>escent</u>	steadily becoming
<u>de</u>-compose	reversal	coni-<u>ferous</u>	bearing
<u>demi</u>-god	half	fanci-<u>ful</u>	full of

Prefix stem and example	Definition of prefix	Suffix stem and example	Definition of suffix
<u>dia</u>-meter	through/during	beauti-<u>fy</u>	to make
<u>dis</u>-like	reversal	widow-<u>hood</u>	state/condition
<u>ex</u>-hale	out of	rept-<u>ile</u>	capable of being
<u>extra</u>-sensory	outside/beyond	redd-<u>ish</u>	relationship/similarity
<u>fore</u>-see	before		
<u>hemi</u>-sphere	half	scept-<u>ism</u>	state/system
<u>homo</u>-logous	same	pharmac-<u>ist</u>	one who does
<u>inter</u>-act	between	hepat-<u>itis</u>	medical: inflammation
<u>intro</u>-spection	inside/into	capabil-<u>ity</u>	state/quality
<u>mal</u>-evolent	bad	civil-<u>ize</u>	to make/act
<u>mega</u>-lopolis	great	gut-<u>less</u>	free from/lacking
<u>micro</u>-dot	small	socio-<u>logy</u>	doctrine/knowledge
<u>mis</u>-fit	wrongly	amuse-<u>ment</u>	state/act of
<u>mono</u>-logue	single/one	thermo-<u>meter</u>	measure of
<u>non</u>-sense	not	matri-<u>mony</u>	condition
<u>ob</u>-struct	in the way	vigil-<u>ance</u>	state/condition
<u>para</u>-graph	beside/near	vigil-<u>ancy</u>	state/quality
<u>per</u>-forate	through	cub-<u>oid</u>	resembling
<u>peri</u>-meter	around/about	conduct-<u>or</u>	one who/thing which
<u>poly</u>-gon	many/much		
<u>post</u>-orbital	after	verb-<u>ose</u>	full of
<u>pre</u>-eminant	before	garrul-<u>ous</u>	full of
<u>pro</u>-vide	before/in front	tele-<u>scope</u>	aid to sight
<u>pseudo</u>-nym	false	censor-<u>ship</u>	state/office of
<u>retro</u>-active	back/backwards	trouble-<u>some</u>	full of/like
<u>semi</u>-breve	half	young-<u>ster</u>	one who/association
<u>sub</u>-editor	under/beneath		
<u>super</u>-sonic	above/over	fanta-<u>sy</u>	state
<u>syn</u>-thesis	with/together	percep-<u>tion</u>	abtract state
<u>tele</u>-cast	distant/far	apti-<u>tude</u>	state/degree of
<u>trans</u>-atlantic	across/beyond	glob-<u>ule</u>	small
<u>ultra</u>-marine	beyond	back-<u>ward</u>	direction
<u>uni</u>-lateral	one	clock-<u>wise</u>	direction/manner
<u>vice</u>-president	in place of	murk-<u>y</u>	condition

Setting attainable goals over a regular course of reading should encourage you to practice and lead to great improvement. Challenge your mind constantly – it needs to be well-nourished, and not simply fed on junk food.

Answers

Test Your Wordpower

Answers

1.c 2.b 3.a 4.a 5.c 6.d 7.a 8.b 9.a 10.d
11.b 12.b 13.c 14.c 15.b 16.a 17.d 18.b 19.a 20.b

Your Score

0-5: Poor. You've probably just got a little lazy over the years – make improving your vocabulary a priority now and you'll soon see what a difference it can make.

6-10: Average. You, too, will benefit from broader knowledge.

11-15: Very good. But keep trying even harder.

16-20: Excellent.

Playing the Detective

Answers

1.e 2.c 3.d 4.a 5.d 6.c
7.b 8.a 9.d 10.e 11.e 12.c

Your Score

Below 6   Poor. But that just means plenty of room for improvement.
7 or 8   Average. Quite acceptable range – keep working on it.
9 or 10   Pretty good. You have a wide vocabulary at your disposal.
11 or 12 Excellent. Although you can never know enough where words are concerned.

Speed Reading

Comprehension:
Answers

1.c   2.b   3.a   4.a   5.b
6.b   7.b   8.a   9.c   10.a

Your Score

Under 7 statements correct: You are perhaps not concentrating as well as you could, or are simply reading too quickly.

7 or more correct: You have a fairly satisfactory level of comprehension – but it could always be better!

To calculate your reading speed:

1. Multiply the number of words in the passage by the number of seconds in an hour, which in this case would be 50,400 (840 x 60).

2. Divide 50,400 by the total number of seconds it took you to read the passage.

So, with a total reading time of 206 seconds, your reading speed would be 245 words per minute.

Your Score

245 words per minute is a fairly average score. A score of around 200 could certainly do with a bit of work, while one of 600 is pretty exceptional.

Understanding

Numbers

The following tests give you the opportunity to assess your numerical skills using the four basic mathematical operations – addition, subtraction, multiplication and division. You have up to 90 minutes to work through the questions. After assessing your skills, read on to discover how to make the numbers in your life work for you.

Replace the question marks to make the string of calculations complete.

1

27	+	?	=	71
				×

84	-	?	=	55	3
=			+		=
?	124	=	?		?
×					-
12	=	?	÷	?	=	69

During a day out shopping for a forthcoming business trip, Sandra bought 12 boxes of Belgian chocolates, priced at $7 each, for which she handed over a money order already made out for $100. She then added the change to the sum of 7 $50 bills and 7 loose dollar bills she had in her wallet. After buying 4 tickets to a show, costing $33 each, how much money did Sandra have left over?

Study the triangles to find the recurring pattern that will enable you to replace the letters with the correct figures.

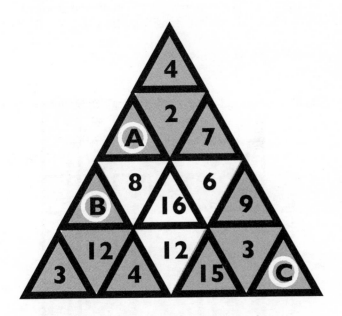

4

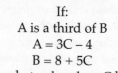

If:
A is a third of B
A = 3C − 4
B = 8 + 5C
then what value does C have?

5

How many seconds will it take for 7 dogs to eat 49 biscuits if they each eat one every 5 seconds?

6

What number comes next in each of the sequences below?

a) 160, 40, 10, ?

b) 7, 22, 67, ?

c) 68, 36, 20, 12, ?

d) 145, 134, 122, 109, ?

e) 33, 24, 34, 23, ?

7

What number replaces the question mark below the grid?

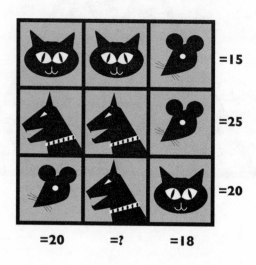

8 How far does the Adams family have to travel to visit their relations if they drive at 60 mph for 20 minutes, spend $3\frac{1}{2}$ hours at a constant 75 mph, and drive for the last 25 minutes at a speed of 40 mph, during which time they stop for 2 minutes to seek directions?

9 Break up each of the following series of numbers, using 2 or 3 of the basic mathematical operations.

a)   2 2 2 2 2 = 66

b)   4 4 4 4 4 = 55

c)   7 7 7 7 7 = 22

d)   6 6 6 6 6 = 11

e)   3 3 3 3 3 = 66

10 If P is half of Q when Q equals the square root of 3 dozen, then what is the numerical value of P?

11 At a birthday party, each child is given some chocolates. There are 6 five-year-olds, 6 six-year-olds and 6 seven-year-olds present. If each child receives 3 times as many chocolates as their age in years, how many chocolates are handed out altogether?

Which symbol would balance the third scale?

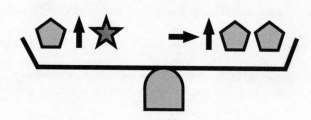

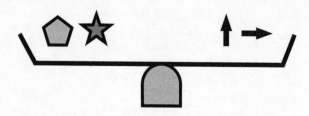

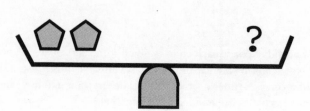

3

If Z is the square of 8, what is X if X is 3 times the value of Y, which is a quarter of Z?

4

On average, 5% of pupils at a particular school are absent each day. With 3 classes of 24, 4 classes of 27 and 5 classes of 32, how many children are expected to attend each day?

5

A clock correctly reads 9:30 on one particular Saturday morning, but then starts to run too fast, gaining 4 minutes each hour indicated. What is the actual time when the clock displays 5 p.m.?

6

Study the 3 pyramids to discover the correct numerical value of each question mark.

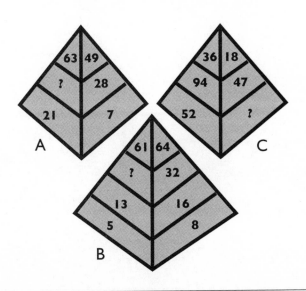

17

Janine invests $200 on January 1st each year in a savings account for her granddaughter. Annual interest of 10% is earned on all the money, payable on December 31st. How much money is in the account on January 2nd in the third year of the account?

18

How much is M worth if 8M − 3N = 29 and 5N − 13 = 32?

19

A desk-making workshop is held one weekend, and various teams from the north and south of the area are taking part. Glue is needed to make these desks. If 60% of the 15 northern teams and 55% of the 20 southern teams managed to obtain it, how many teams are left without glue?

According to the other 2 pictures, how many birds do the 3 clouds lack?

21 What do S and T equal if 4R = 6S = 8T and 7R = 42?

22 A cube-shaped swimming pool is drained to change the water. The water had a depth of exactly 5 feet.
How long will it take to empty the pool if the water level decreases by 3 inches every 4 minutes?

> **Multiplication is vexation, Division is as bad; The rule of three doth puzzle me, And practice drives me mad.** (Anon.)

If the prospect of confronting a page crammed with figures makes you shudder, you are not alone. Numbers can fill the most literate and educated of people with fear, but you will soon discover that most of these fears are groundless.

After working through the self-assessment section, you may already have realized that most of the tests are much simpler than they first appeared. Consider the shopping problem. Delete all the extraneous text and you are left with a few basic figures from which a simple series of calculations lead you to the answer.

The most important things to remember when dealing with numbers are:

○ Don't panic

○ Keep things simple

Whether attempting problems like the ones included here, or sifting through mounds of paperwork to work out your disposable income, keep the data as simple and well organized as possible.

Building Barriers

We are bombarded with numbers in one form or another from a very young age. As children, we can easily work out that one of the 6 parts of a certain game is missing or that our pocket money is short by a certain amount. We happily count up to large numbers during a game of hide-and-seek. Yet as soon as numbers are connected with school and work, our previously casual attitude is often transformed.

Once we are criticized for a careless mathematical error, the fear of making further mistakes often causes us to build a complete mental barricade where any numbers are concerned. Such fear inevitably prevents progress, encouraging a loathing for the subject, and a refusal to learn.

The power of your brain cannot be underestimated. You may wonder at the sophistication and speed with which today's computers hurry through complicated calculations, but creating a computer with the abilities of the human mind would be impossible. The size of such a machine would be unmanageable – as would the instruction manual! So have confidence in yourself next time you are faced with pages of calculations. Don't always reach for a calculator – take the opportunity to make your mind work harder, and the practice will soon start to make a difference.

Making Numbers Work for You

Despite the "vexation" that mathematics may provoke, it is actually a simplification of everyday life. Numbers often act as a straightforward code for much more complex ideas, so the notion that you can't tackle them at all would  seem to be completely illogical. How often have you switched on the news to hear a lengthy description of a company's performance that could have been represented far more succinctly by a graph? Of course numbers and statistics can always be manipulated and used to impress – mainly because most people are too afraid of figures to question them. So don't believe another person's calculations as a matter of course – be on your guard!

From building the Great Pyramids to the latest advances in computer technology, mathematics has always played an important part of human life. Each advance has the potential to bring further benefit, so concentrate on making numbers work for you, and don't simply shy away from them.

To do or not to do – that is the question. It is impossible to master any level of mathematics by just reading about it. Being confident with numbers requires practice and experimentation. If the very idea makes you nervous, don't automatically reject it before giving it a go. A little practice can rapidly lead to heartening results. As with any game, you have to learn the rules before you start to play.

The number tips that follow are designed simply as an aid to basic numeracy – it's up to you to decide how far you need to take it.

Multiplication and Division

Does the mere mention of "multiplication tables" bring back some of your least cherished childhood memories, of schooldays filled with endless repetition and tests? If so, don't despair. Multiplication is very useful in everyday life, as you find when you need to work out how much 6 boxes of chocolates at $7 each will cost during a Christmas shopping spree. Chances are, you will tackle the necessary calculations very effectively, because there is no teacher peering over your desk, pressurizing you for an answer; no one ready to laugh at your mistakes. If you take your time, and make a point of working things out in your head, rapid multiplication could soon become second nature.

For simple calculations, a multiplication and division table is provided below for your reference. To multiply two numbers together, go down the column of one until you meet the row of the other to arrive at the answer. So, 6 lots of $7 costs $42. For division, go down the column headed with the smaller number until you find the larger number that is to be divided into. The row number gives the answer. So, if you have 72 inches of timber that you want to divide into 8-inch lengths, working down column 8 until you reach 72 shows that you will have 9 lengths altogether. But if you have 90 inches and still want 8-inch lengths, find the number closest to 90 in column 8 (which is 88) to discover that you can cut 11 complete lengths with 2 inches of timber left over.

COLUMN

ROW	2	3	4	5	6	7	8	9	10	11	12	13	14	15
2	4	6	8	10	12	14	16	18	20	22	24	26	28	30
3	6	9	12	15	18	21	24	27	30	33	36	39	42	45
4	8	12	16	20	24	28	32	36	40	44	48	52	56	60
5	10	15	20	25	30	35	40	45	50	55	60	65	70	75
6	12	18	24	30	36	42	48	54	60	66	72	78	84	90
7	14	21	28	35	42	49	56	63	70	77	84	91	98	105
8	16	24	32	40	48	56	64	72	80	88	96	104	112	120
9	18	27	36	45	54	63	72	81	90	99	108	117	126	135
10	20	30	40	50	60	70	80	90	100	110	120	130	140	150
11	22	33	44	55	66	77	88	99	110	121	132	143	154	165
12	24	36	48	60	72	84	96	108	120	132	144	156	168	180
13	26	39	52	65	78	91	104	117	130	143	156	169	182	195
14	28	42	56	70	84	98	112	126	140	154	168	182	196	210
15	30	45	60	75	90	105	120	135	150	165	180	195	210	225

Sometimes problems can actually be solved more quickly without the use of a table, or even a calculator. This is especially true when dealing with the numbers 5 and 10. For example, if you want to buy 10 notebooks priced at $4.50 each, you will be spending $45:

4.5 x 10 = 45

To multiply a decimal number by 10, all you have to do is move the decimal point one place to the right. If you are working with a whole number, all you have to do is add a nought: 10 boxes each containing 12 pens hold 120 pens in total.

It therefore follows that, to divide by 10, you remove a nought (if there is one) or shift a decimal point one place to the left. Where a whole number such as 45 is concerned, it is sometimes easier to view it as 45.0, so that the position of the decimal point is clear in your mind.

When dealing with the number 5, remind yourself that it is simply half of 10. So, if you are multiplying by 5, add a nought to the relevant number, or shift the decimal point to the right, and then divide by 2. Five of the notebooks priced at $4.50 cost $22.50:

4.5 x 10 = 45

45 ÷ 2 = 22.5

To divide the 120 pens between 5 people is just a case of common sense – doubling 120 and dividing that by 10. Knowing how to multiply a number by 10 gives you enough information to deal with both multiplication and division involving the numbers 5, 10, and other related numbers, too. Some of these are summarized below. For division, follow the same process but in reverse.

To multiply by:	add this many noughts:	and divide by: (multiply by)
5	**1**	**2**
10	**1**	**1**
20	**1**	**(2)**
25	**2**	**4**
100	**2**	**1**
1000	**3**	**1**

Getting to Grips With Fractions

Whether dividing a cake into equal portions, or understanding statistics in a newspaper report, you probably have to deal with fractions every day, although you may not be aware of it. They are easy to cope with as long as you know the logical rules.

Multiplication

Can you remember the rule for multiplying fractions from your schooldays? Even if you can't, the chances are that you know how to do this instinctively. If you had to divide a cake into 2, you would cut it in half; if you had to share that cake between 4 people, you would cut it into quarters. So you obviously know that half of a half is a quarter. Expressed mathematically:

$$\frac{1}{2} \times \frac{1}{2} = \frac{1}{4}$$

This is simply a case of multiplying the numbers above the line (the numerators) together, and the numbers below the line (the denominators) together. This rule applies to any fractions:

$$\frac{2}{3} \times \frac{3}{4} = \frac{6}{12}$$

In this case, for example, if you divide ³/₄ of a cake three ways, two of those portions together make one full half.

The fraction ⁶/₁₂ can easily be simplified. When both the numbers above and below the line can be divided exactly by the same whole number, that number can be deleted, or cancelled out. This is because multiplying both parts of the fraction by the same number does not alter the value of the fraction. So:

$$\frac{6}{12} = \frac{6 \times 1}{6 \times 2} = \frac{1}{2}$$

Division

Dividing one fraction by another is made easy by simply knowing one useful trick. Just swap one fraction's components around, and multiply by the other. Say you have 2 cakes, each of a different size. One cake fits $1\frac{1}{2}$ times into 3/4 of another:

$$\frac{3}{4} \div \frac{1}{2} = \frac{3}{4} \times \frac{2}{1} = \frac{6}{4} = 1\frac{1}{2}$$

Addition and Subtraction

If you want to add 2 fractions, and both have the same number below the line, get your answer by simply adding together the 2 numbers above the line. This is totally logical when you consider that combining the 2 halves of a broken plate makes 1 whole plate. This would be expressed mathematically as:

$$\frac{1}{2} + \frac{1}{2} = \frac{1+1}{2} = 1 \text{ and } \underline{not} \frac{1+1}{2+2} \text{ which equals } \frac{2}{4} \text{ or } \frac{1}{2}$$

As already shown, multiplying both parts of a fraction by the same number does not affect its value. So to make the numbers below the line on both fractions the same, multiply both parts of one fraction by the number below the line, or denominator, of the other. This may sound confusing, but when expressed mathematically, the process should become much clearer:

$$\frac{1}{2} + \frac{3}{4} = \frac{4\times1}{4\times2} + \frac{3\times2}{4\times2} = \frac{4+6}{4\times2} = \frac{10}{8} = 1\frac{2}{8} = 1\frac{1}{4}$$

Once you have overcome any needless fear of fractions, you can see from the examples above that they can greatly simplify what would otherwise be extremely complex problems if, for example, they were expressed entirely in words.

What's the Point of Percentages?

Fractions can easily be expressed as percentages. A percentage is a proportion of a whole, and that whole is 100 – "per" means "for" and "cent" means 100. We are continually bombarded with percentages: 25% reduction on sale goods; 67% examination pass rate; 8% of a town's population unemployed. Because they sound so important, many people are intimidated by them, but they are really just a way of measuring information so that you can get an accurate picture.

In order to convert a fraction into a percentage, just multiply it by 100. So, if 3/4 of those attending your evening class passed the French exam, you know that:

$$\frac{3}{4} \times 100 = \frac{300}{4} = 75$$

This means that 75% of the students passed, or 3 out of every 4 people. So logically, dividing a percentage by 100 produces the corresponding fraction:

$$75\% = \frac{75}{100} = \frac{3}{4}$$

When calculations involve percentages, it is essential that these are converted into fractions rather than just omitting the percentage symbol. Otherwise, you may get rather more than you bargained for!

Discounts

You will often come across percentages when dealing with special offers on goods. When you want to work out how much you save by buying a washing machine priced at $450 that is reduced in price by 12%, all you have to do is:

divide the original price by 100, and then multiply by the percentage in question, or

12 x $4.50 = $54

To find the price you will pay, simply take $54 away from the original price to give $396.

If you just want to find the final price, you can divide the original price by 100, and multiply that by 100 minus the discount offered: **100 – 12 = 88%** An easy tip to remember every time you have to deal with fractions or percentages is that "of" in this context means "multiply".
So 88% of 200 is

$$\frac{88}{100} \times 200 = 176$$

Price Plus Percentage

To calculate a price that needs to include an additional percentage, for example if you had to add a tax of 20% onto the price of goods, follow this routine:

Calculate the 20% as before, and then add it to the original price. If you have a calculator handy, or you want a bit of a challenge, then the original price can be multiplied by 1 plus the percentage divided by 100.

So, the final cost of a tool costing $80 with a tax of 20% can be written as:

80 x 1.2 = $96

Positive and Negative Numbers

Whenever you sit down to work out the current state of your finances, you are using positive and negative numbers. Any bills you have to pay are negative; your income is positive. Yet the two may easily be confused. Just as the further a positive number is away from nought, the larger it is, the further a negative number is away from nought, the smaller it is: –1000 is smaller than –10.

If you have two bills to pay, one of $70 and one of $45, you have a total bill of $115. So adding 2 negative numbers together still results in a negative number. Expressed mathematically:

(–70) + (–45) = –115   The brackets help to avoid confusion.

But, if you have only one bill of $70, and have been paid $100, you clearly have $30 left over after settling your debts:

(–70) + 100 = 30

In this way, you can begin to see that, if the positive value is greater than the negative, you are left with a positive value, and vice versa.

Now, if $30 of the bill for $70 is found to have been a result of overcharging, you must take the $30 away from the $70 to find that you only have $40 to pay:

(–70) – (–30) = (–70) + 30 = –40

Now you can also see how 2 minuses make a plus. Perhaps it is simpler than it first appeared after all!

The Simplest Things in Life

Were you intimidated by the predominantly wordy problems in the self-assessment section? If so, take heart from knowing that a good dose of common sense and logic can be just as helpful as mathematical expertise. Consider the problems below. Would you be able to give an immediate answer?

1. Your boss asks you for a rough evaluation of the results of a survey set up to find out how many teenagers are likely to watch less than 25 hours of television each week. If approximately 30% of those asked were found to spend more than 25 hours a week watching television, and 3/4 of a group of 420 teenagers were questioned, what answer would you give your boss?

Don't panic! A rough answer means just that. Try working backward: 3/4 of 420 is approximately 300. 30% is roughly 1/3, so about 100 teenagers out of the 300 fall into the more-than-25-hour category. A sensible answer would therefore be: **300 – 100 = 200**.

2. You're working to a tight schedule. You've spent just over 2/3 of a 5-day working week on a project, and have got about 15% of it done. You think that the last half, being more complicated, will take double the time. How many weeks do you think it will take to complete the project altogether?

If 15% takes just over 2/3 of a week, then the first 50% equals about 3 lots of this, namely 2 weeks. So the second half takes about 4, and the whole project takes about 6 weeks in total.

Go It Alone

Now build on the hints in the previous pages to try some problems out for yourself.

1. You inherit a share of the fortune of your uncle's cousin once-removed. Three properties, each valued at $155,000 and 4 cars, each worth about 1/3 of each property, together with shares valued at just under $150,000, form the fortune. If you are entitled to 12%, approximately how much is your inheritance worth?

2. You are trying to ascertain roughly how much cash you will have to live on at the end of the month. You are currently $240 in credit, but have a credit card bill of 2/5 of that to pay at the end of the month, when your salary of $1,250 is paid in. However, you always set 25% of your salary aside to go into your savings account. How much do you reckon on being able to spend?

Answers

1. $27 + (44) = 71 \times 3 = (213) - 69 = (144) / (12) = 12 \times (7) = 84 - (29)$
   $= 55 + (69) = 124.$

2. $241

3. A = 14 B = 9 C = 5

Consider each of the 4 larger triangles in turn; each one is subdivided into 4 smaller ones. Multiply the number at the apex of each large triangle by the number in its base triangle, moving in a clockwise direction. Divide the number you get by the number in the next small base triangle to give the number in the small central triangle. The central large triangle is upside down.

4. C = 5

5. 35 seconds

6. a) 2.5 (quartered)
   b) 202 (x3, +1, or +15, +45, +135.)
   c) 8 (halved, +2, or −32, −16, −8.)
   d) 95 (−11, −12, −13.)
   e) 35 (−9, +10, −11, +12.)

7. 22.
   Cats = 4, mice = 7, dogs = 9

8. 297.8 miles

9. a) $22 \times 2 + 22 = 66$
   b) $44 / 4 + 44 = 55$
   c) $(77 + 77) / 7 = 22$
   d) $(66 + 6 − 6) / 6 = 11$
   e) $33 \times 3 − 33 = 66$

10. 3

11. 324

12. One arrow pointing up

13. 48

14. 323

15. 4:30 p.m.

16. a) 42 (add 21, working upward on each side)
    b) 29 (left number + right number = number above left number.
       Left number + 3 = right number)
    c) 26 (right number is worth half of the corresponding left number)
17. $662
18. 7
19. 15
20. 6 (2 birds per cloud; 3 per sun)
21. S = 4, T = 3
22. 1 hour 20 minutes (80 minutes)

Your Score

0-14 Quite poor – but a little work will soon show a rapid improvement.

15-20 Average. You have made a promising start, so keep going!

21-26 Good. You have obviously found the right approach for dealing with numbers.

27-32 Excellent.

Go It Alone

Answers

1. $3 \times 150 + 4 \times 50 + 150 = 800$. Fortune worth about $800,000.
    $12\% = $ about $\frac{1}{8} = $ about $100,000

2. $\frac{2 \times 250}{5} = 100$. So $150 after credit card. Approximate $1250 to $1200; 75%
    of which is $900. Left with 900 + 150, about $1050.

Increase Your

Intelligence

It's a wonderful moment when a sudden insight flashes into your mind, perhaps solving some troublesome problem or conjuring up an ingenious idea. Creative thinking paves the way for a more exciting, less problematic and often more successful life. See how you fare with the creativity self-assessment tests below. Scoring for all these exercises is on page 260.

Objective Thinking

Consider the list of objects below. Each has its own particular purpose, but your task is to imagine as many other ways as possible that it could be of some use – the more unusual, the better. For example, a submarine would obviously play its part in naval work, but could also serve as a giant incubating chamber for scientific experiments. Dedicate 5 minutes to each object. Feel free to dismantle, rearrange, fill up, transport to an unexpected environment...

1. An empty cassette case.

2. A filing cabinet.

3. Sydney Opera House.

4. A giraffe.

5. A contact lens.

6. A set of scaffolding.

7. A washing-up liquid container.

8. An electric guitar.

9. The Eiffel Tower.

10. The planet Mars.

Playing with Images

The following phrases conjure up a certain kind of visual image. It's up to you to identify up to 3 equivalent phrases that correspond to each image given. You have 3 minutes to find the most apt and original equivalents for each one.

Example

A balloon let loose in the sky.
Could be conceptually synonymous with:

a. A twig floating on the ocean.
b. A prisoner on being released.
c. A painter facing a blank canvas.

Now try these:

1. Viewing a tennis match from a helicopter above.

2. Losing your voice mid-conversation.

3. A sudden thunderstorm.

4. Climbing a ladder.

5. Hearing a fire alarm.

6. Diving into the sea.

7. A derelict house.

8. Water in a bath draining away.

9. Goldfish in a tank.

10. Leaves of a book flapping in the breeze.

Storytime

If you are happier with words than images, you may find that the following task is a better test of your creative spirit. You are allowed up to 300 words to create a smooth, easily understood narrative. It doesn't matter whether it's fact or fiction, just as long as it makes sense! Seems simple? Well, there's one small additional task you have – as many items as possible from the list below must somehow be woven into the thread of your text. The timing is up to you – this is an opportunity for your imagination to roam freely.

Items to include:

1. A toothbrush.

2. A wild animal.

13. A battle – verbal, physical or otherwise.

4. A long journey.

5. A personal catastrophe.

6. Water.

7. A long telephone call.

8. The acquisition of money.

9. Learning a new skill.

10. An art gallery.

11. A tub of cream.

12. A dictionary.

13. The police.

14. A chance encounter.

15. A candle.

Picture This

Here's another test for the visually creative among you. Study each of the diagrams below for 1 minute, listing as many interpretations as possible of what each one represents.

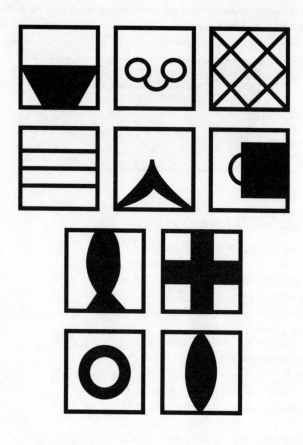

Creativity

Whether it is interpreted as producing totally new ideas or combining old ideas in a new way, creativity is something that many of us admire and try to acquire. The exact nature and source of creativity seems to be something of a mystery. Its scientific origin has failed to be precisely determined, and many scientists would say that any definite understanding of exactly what it is will always remain a puzzle.

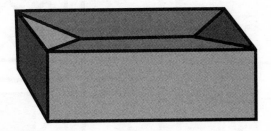

What is It?

Some studies suggest that high levels of creativity are related to the way an otherwise typical nervous system functions, rather than to the structure itself. Perhaps it is because of this uncertainty that a diverse display of creativity continues to flourish. If 'rules' about the precise nature of creativity were to be laid down, this might well stifle all kinds of interesting ideas.

There are, however, various factors that we are fairly certain affect creativity. We know that being able to escape preconceptions, conditioning and convention is a key for fresh thought – who said that the average vehicle has to have four wheels? Past experience and knowledge can help us, and often prevents us from making mistakes, but it can also stop us from trying new paths of thought. The very young are generally less inhibited about changing the rules – because they don't yet know what many of them are.

Early Influences

Childhood plays a vital role in determining our future level of creativity. Everyone is thought to have some creative capacity, so nurturing this skill from an early age can reap huge benefits in later life. The early years can provide a wealth of creative opportunities, and if children are encouraged to explore these actively, rewards are bound to follow later in life. If a parent constantly imposes their view on a child, it will take a very strong-minded child to resist these and forge their own ideas.

Like intelligence, creativity usually lasts into old age – and it may even prolong life. But intelligence is not necessarily related to creativity. Rather than being particularly special, the basic skills that seem to be linked with creativity are actually very ordinary: noticing, recollecting and recognizing. How these are manipulated, however, is where creativity comes in.

Staying Power

Creative success is predominantly the result of sustained effort and motivation rather than any miraculous power – you cannot become a virtuoso jazz pianist overnight! Technical ability plays no less a part than natural talent and significant displays of creativity are unlikely to appear before a decade of dedicated effort. So, child prodigies do not suddenly acquire their ability from nowhere – they simply started before everybody else! This relentless drive often stems from an endless curiosity, an experimental nature, and an overriding desire to break away from the work of predecessors.

Confidence is a vital factor. It takes courage to break away from convention. As we all know, some of the greatest inventions and ideas of our times were considered insane when they were first put forward.

Winging It

Improvising solutions to problems that present no obvious explanation is a sure sign of creative thought. However, this obviously requires a great deal of knowledge and experience – pure creativity stems from learning, but is impossible to learn.

Exactly when, where and how a creative idea is born cannot be scientifically predicted. A sudden flash of insight can come into the mind, seemingly from nowhere, although what has probably happened is that the brain has been working away with the idea subconsciously. The creation of an original idea is therefore ongoing. Your initial confrontation with a problem may appear to be unproductive, but this can have the effect of granting your brain unrestricted freedom to play around with it. From this may come that moment of sudden inspiration, culminating in a rational appraisal of the idea. All that remains to be done is to convince others of your genius!

All of this means that no one, regardless of their abilities, can be relied upon to come up with an appropriate idea at exactly the right moment. Nevertheless, a person's overall creativity is still likely to remain relatively consistent.

Creative Confusion

Creativity can occasionally be confused with ideas that seem original but that actually follow a text-book formula. Editing an existing musical composition, adding bits here and there to make the whole piece appear to be new, is far less creative than composing the piece in the first place. There are countless rules that we all stick to, from how we structure a sentence to how we build a house. Most of us are simply embellishing these when we work, rather than creating the rules themselves.

Whether used to master a particular activity, or merely to cope more efficiently with daily life, an actively creative mind can enhance a range of other mental pursuits. For example, creativity allows much greater abilities of recall. When a topic is approached with an unusual, individual slant, the brain can often access information more quickly. A creative mind is usually a questioning and curious one, in which interest and motivation are kept actively alive and ideas create the desire to discover even more.

Getting Your Point Across

Creativity is all very well, but unless you can persuade others of your talents, it can easily go unnoticed and unappreciated. People might not have the knowledge necessary to understand your ideas, or may be reluctant to accept new ideas. So, it's often not just a question of being creative, but of being able to communicate concepts to those around you.

Testing it Out

If allowed room to breathe, creativity is likely to last a lifetime. A conscious effort to maintain your creativity inevitably leads to a life organized in such a way that your creative performance is maximized. If you face each new problem positively, considering how it could be overcome successfully rather than stating that it is simply impossible to solve, creativity will flow much more easily. But patience is essential – creative ideas need time to hatch and grow; they cannot be expected to appear magically whenever you click your fingers!

The Merits of Motivation

Because you need time and the right opportunities to cultivate your creative spirit, no one can be expected to come up with wonderful ideas on a regular basis throughout his or her lifetime. It will always help if you focus your attention on what you enjoy, rather than what you feel you should be attending to. Try to concentrate on a limited area, rather than casually dipping into a medley of subjects. Devotion to a particular area of interest enables the mind to work through ideas that require considerable time and effort to come to fruition.

Motivation is more likely to thrive if the main force of it comes from you, rather than from outside influences. Being genuinely fascinated by something for its own sake, and not simply because of the rewards it can bring, for example, usually brings a greater depth of creativity. Your surroundings, however, do play an important part. Feeling psychologically safe and free to explore can work wonders. Also, while we shouldn't feel too restricted by other people's demands in order to be truly creative, a little support and praise from others can have a dramatic effect.

The Old and the New

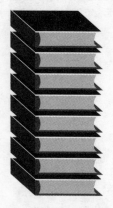

Although you may view creativity as a matter of producing something fresh, give yourself the best possible start by knowing as much as possible about existing ideas before embarking on anything new. A degree of technical knowledge can open your mind up to a wealth of new ideas, sparking off thoughts that may never have occurred to you before. Look at existing information from various perspectives to help you to break away from safe, tried and tested ideas.

Don't let other people's negative reactions automatically interfere with your creative urges.
Try to understand and develop your real strengths and talents, and this will give you greater self-confidence. Self-belief and risk-taking form the essence of creative success. Just looking around you and seeing the range of objects that have originated from someone's creative ingenuity can only serve as an enticement for you to follow suit.

Breaking Away

Approach each creative challenge on your own terms. Try to break away from existing limitations to develop your own interpretation of each task that you face. Too often people restrict themselves by working within a problem rather than reaching out and beyond it. This is illustrated by the exercise below.
You may well be familiar with this puzzle, which asks you to join up all the dots with four straight lines without removing your pen from the paper. The solution is on page 261.

Brainstorming

Brainstorming serves as a tremendous aid in improving creativity; decide whether you prefer to do it on your own or with other people. Try simply noting down any thought and association that comes to mind when you focus on a specific task – no matter how bizarre it might seem. You may find that the mere act of writing down the relevant issue in the middle of a blank piece of paper, and creating a web of related ideas branching out from this produces more than enough ideas ready to pursue. Or, if you are working with others, you might simply throw ideas around out loud – perhaps playing word association games and so on. Brainstorming itself needn't be a lengthy process – it is the development of each thought that may take some time.

Whether you are alone or generating ideas with others, relax and let your ideas flow. Speaking continuously, simply saying whatever springs to mind, activates the brain encouraging ideas. Whether your words contain the beginnings of a promising idea, or merely show that no ideas are forthcoming, is irrelevant – take heart from knowing that even the most creative mind lapses every now and again!

In brainstorming sessions, don't:

○ stop to worry whether what you are saying is grammatical or beautifully expressed
○ feel that you have to justify every thought – in the early stages, simply the fact that you have come up with it yourself makes an idea justifiable; it is only later, after further deliberation, than you need to defend it against possible opposition.

Develop your thoughts as you experience them, as opposed to relating them or writing them down later. Thinking and speaking simultaneously can enable a chain of thoughts to unwind and gradually move toward its full potential. Regardless of whether your chosen instrument is a pen or a paintbrush, music or science, a positive approach and determination help to maximize success. Leave it to others to set the limits and restrictions – telling yourself you can't do it only adds to your obstacles. Don't be your own worst enemy!

Answers

Objective Thinking

Your Score

Only you, or preferably an unbiased volunteer, can judge the quality of your responses. However, as a general guide:

0–4 uses for each object: Poor. You probably just need to relax more and your creative ideas will flow more readily.
5–8: Good. You are obviously used to looking at things from all kinds of angles.
Above 8: Excellent.

Playing with Images

Scoring

Award yourself points as follows (or get an obliging friend to help):

0 for failing to respond, or producing an inappropriate, unrelated response.
1 for an appropriate but unoriginal answer (example response: a)
2 points for an appropriate and more original answer (example response: b)
3 points for an appropriate and highly original, imaginative answer (example response: c)
0-40: Poor. Again, you'll find this much easier if you relax and stop looking for the 'right' answer.
41-65: Good. You've got good creative potential but you tend to hold back. Dare to be more adventurous with your ideas!
66-90: Excellent.

Storytime

Scoring

That helpful friend will come in handy again! Starting with a score of 15, deduct one point for the omission of each item. Now award a score out of 5 (5 being the best) for:

a. How well the text flows and general clarity.

b. Degree of interest/amusement/enjoyment derived from your story.

c. Level of original and imaginative thought.

Your Score

0-16: Poor. Your creative muscles just need a bit of exercise.

17-23: Good. Now see how much further you can take your creative ideas.

24-30: Excellent.

Picture This

Your Score.

For each diagram:

0-3 interpretations: Poor.

4-6: Good.

7 or over: Excellent.

Breaking Away

Most people approach this first by restricting the lines to the square itself; the solution demands that the pen breaks away from the confines of the square. Make sure that, whenever you face a new challenge, you don't always trap yourself within a limiting square.

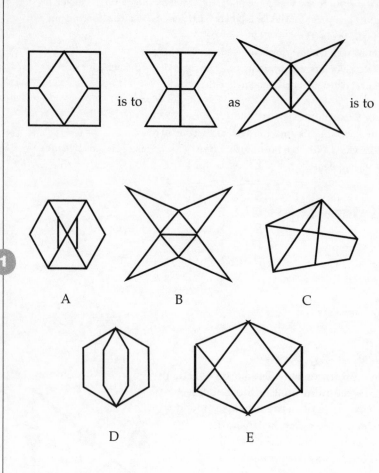

is to ... as ... is to

A

B

C

D

E

If one letter in each of the four words below is changed, a phrase can be found. What is it?

AN SHE ODE LAND

Complete the three-letter words, which, reading down, will reveal a bird.

E	L	(	•	)
A	I	(	•	)
S	E	(	•	)
G	E	(	•	)
S	K	(	•	)
D	I	(	•	)
P	E	(	•	)
D	U	(	•	)

A farmer with 240 yards of fencing wishes to enclose a rectangular area of the greatest possible size. What will be the greatest area surrounded?

Four of the pieces below can be fitted together to form a square. What is the odd one out?

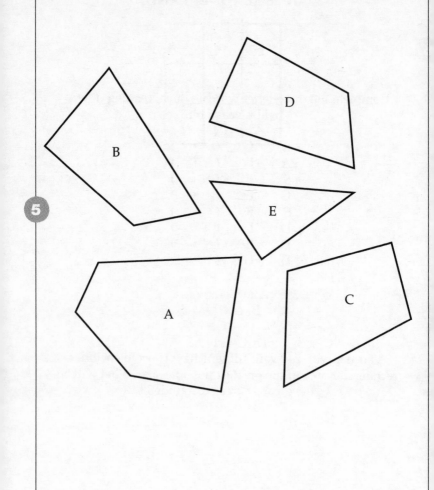

Start at a corner square and move in a clockwise spiral
to the middle to spell out a nine-letter word.
What are the missing letters?

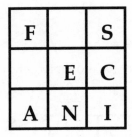

What word is a synonym of PRINCIPLE?

A. MAJESTY
B. AXIOM
C. COST
D. CAPITAL
E. LEADER

8

Find two words with different spellings, but which sound alike, that can mean:

CESSATION / SNATCH

9

What number should replace the question mark?

5	6	1
?	4	8
7	2	3

A. 0
B. 1
C. 2
D. 3
E. 4

10

A three-word phrase, below, has had each word's initial letter removed. What is the phrase?

ETTASE

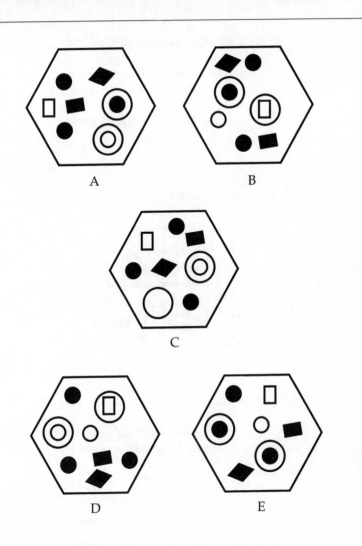

Which of the above hexagons is the odd one out?

What is the odd one out?

A. PEW
B. PULPIT
C. FONT
D. TERMAGENT
E. AISLE

What number should replace the question mark?

What word is an antonym of CULPABLE?

A. INNOCENT
B. LIABLE
C. ERUDITE
D. CREDULOUS
E. FLATTERING

What word is a synonym of IMBROGLIO?

A. ENVY
B. FOOLISHNESS
C. ENTANGLEMENT
D. SPECTACULAR
E. DUPLICITY

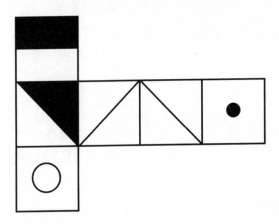

When the above is folded to form a cube, one of the figures below can be produced. What is it?

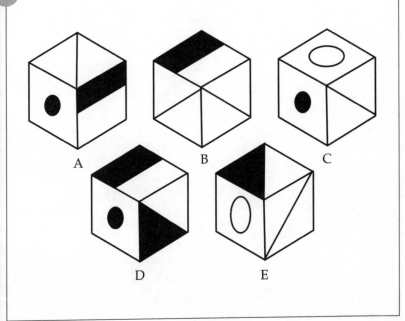

A   B   C

D   E

What word can be placed in front of the other five to form five new words or phrases? Each dot represents a letter.

17

$(\bullet \bullet \bullet \bullet)$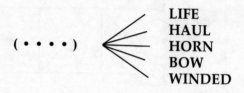

LIFE
HAUL
HORN
BOW
WINDED

Find a six-letter word made up of only the following four letters?

18

B E
U J

Which of the following is the odd one out?

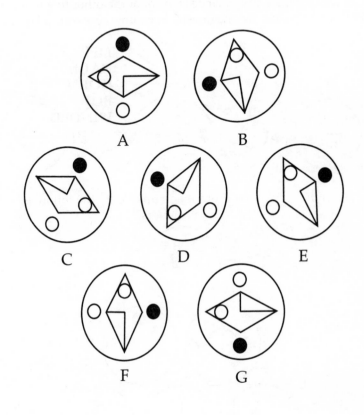

A

B

C

D

E

F

G

Place two three-letter segments together to form a
weather term.

HYR MET COM ISO ZEP THE

Which of the circles below should replace
the question mark?

A   B   C   D   E

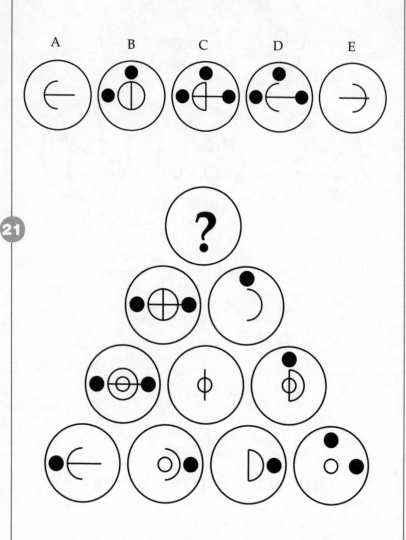

21

Which of the following is the opposite of TORPID?

22

        A.   SHALLOW
        B.   CYCLOPEAN
        C.   ELORITCH
        D.   SQUAMOUS
        E.   ENERGETIC

Which of the following words is the odd one out?

23

A. CAPRICIOUS
B. FICKLE
C. ARBITRARY
D. SPURIOUS
E. INCONSTANT

24

What number should complete the series and replace the question mark?

73614   4637   764   ?

A word can be placed in the brackets that has the same meaning as the words outside. What is it? Each dot represents a letter.

A TRIFLE (• • • • • • • • •) BALL GAME

If the missing letters in the circle below are correctly inserted they will form an eight-letter word. The word will not necessarily have to be read in a clockwise direction, but the letters are in order. What is the word and missing letters?

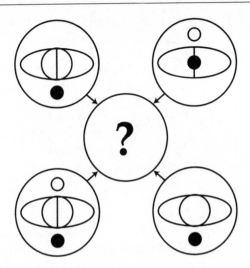

Each line and symbol that appears in the four outer circles, above, is transferred to the middle circle according to how many times it appears, as follows

One time — it is transferred
Two times — it is possibly transferred
Three times — it is transferred
Four times — it is not transferred

Which of the circles below should appear in the middle circle?

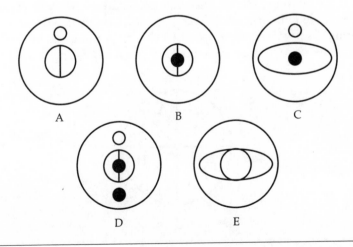

Find a 10-letter word using adjoining letters once each only.

28

A FARRAGO is a type of what?

29

A. MESS
B. DANCE
C. PLAIN
D. WHEAT
E. DINGO

If the missing letters in the circle below are correctly inserted they will form an eight-letter word. The word will not necessarily have to be read in a clockwise direction, but the letters are in order. What is the word and missing letters?

30

Answers

D.

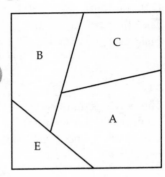

E. The right and left halves of the figure switch positions as illustrated below:

1

On the one hand.

2

Flamingo. The completed words are: elF, aiL, seA, geM, skI, diN, peG, duO.

3

3600 yards^2. Divide the 240 yards by 4 to get 60 yards each side, so 60 x 60 = 3600.

4

5

6 Fascinate. The missing letters are A and T.

7 B (axiom).

8 Rest and wrest.

9 A (0). The sum of each horizontal, vertical, and diagonal line equals 12.

10 Set at ease.

D.
The others contain only one small white circle, while this one has two.

18 Jujube.

19 G. The others form identical pairs in different rotations: A&F, B&C, D&E.

12 D (termagent).
The others are inside the main part of a church.

20 Zephyr (a wind).

375.
The previous number doubled, then at each stage 1, 2, 3, 4, 5, 6, and 7, respectively, is added.

21 C.
Different symbols in adjoining circles on the same row are carried into the circle between them in the row above. Similar symbols in the same place are dropped.

13
$1 + 1 + 1 = 3$;
$3 + 3 + 2 = 8$;
$8 + 8 + 3 = 19$;
$19 + 19 + 4 = 42$;
$42 + 42 + 5 = 89$;
$89 + 89 + 6 = 184$;
$184 + 184 + 7 = 375$.

22 E (energetic).

23 D (spurious, which means false). The others mean irregular or unreliable.

14 A (innocent).

15 C (entanglement).

24 67.
The order of numbers reverses and the lowest digit is dropped.

16 C.

17 Long.

25 Bagatelle.

26 Maniacal.
The missing letters are
M and I.

27 D.

28 Cloudiness.

39 A (a mess).

30 Yashmaks.
The missing letters are
Y and M.

Four of the five pieces below can be fitted together to form a decagon. Which is the odd one out?

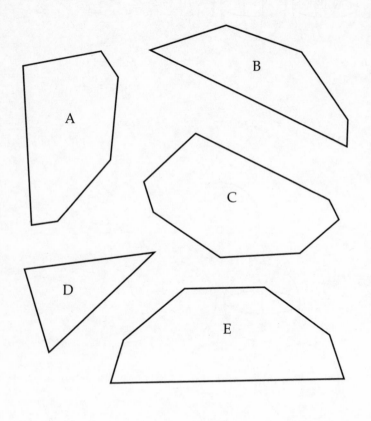

1

Which of the circles, A, B, C, D, or E, should replace the question mark below?

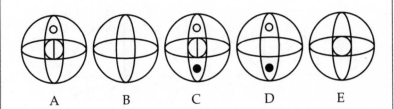

A   B   C   D   E

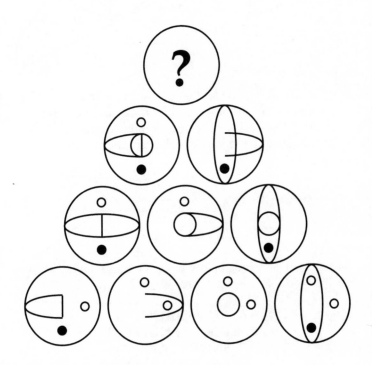

If the missing letters in the two circles below are correctly inserted they will form synonymous words. The words are read in a clockwise direction, and the letters are in order. What are the words and missing letters?

A chandler collected candle ends until he had 2197. How many candles in total could he make and burn from these if 13 candles ends make up one candle, and all subsequent ends are collected and reused?

WAVE : GESTICULATE

Which pair of words below have the same relationship as the words above?

A. RUN : SAUNTER
B. KICK : GENUFLECT
C. SNORE : ANNOY
D. LAUGH : CHANT
E. WINK : NICTITATE

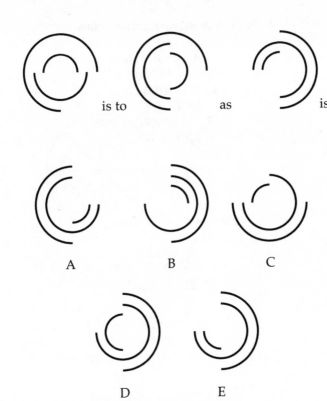

A B C

D E

What number is missing from the third column?

18 24 54

15 40 15

6   3   ?

What two words are antonymous?

A. SALUBRIOUS
B. FRETTING
C. WORRIED
D. BUSY
E. STRONG
F. NOXIOUS

What is the odd one out?

A. HOLE
B. ICE
C. ELEPHANT
D. OUT
E. SEA

4986 : 1314 : 45

What series has the same relationship as the one above?

A. 2386 : 1314 : 45
B. 7842 : 1513 : 64
C. 7217 : 1862 : 34
D. 9875 : 1217 : 83
E. 8795 : 1514 : 65

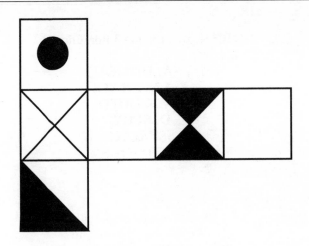

When the above is folded to form a cube, one of the figures below can be produced. What is it?

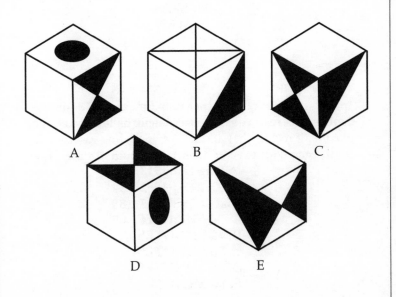

A   B   C

D   E

KNIFE is to CUT as CLEAVER is to?

A. SEVER
B. LACERATE
C. CHOP
D. SLICE
E. IMPALE

12

What word belongs with:

AGE   PORT   ABLE   WORD

A. LIKE
B. OVER
C. KIND
D. ARM
E. MAN

13

In a game of 12 players that lasts for exactly 75 minutes there are six reserves who alternate equally with starting players. It means that all players, including reserves, are in the game for exactly the same amount of time. How long is this?

14

A. 30 MINUTES
B. 40 MINUTES
C. 50 MINUTES
D. 55 MINUTES
E. 60 MINUTES

What two words are synonymous?

A. NOISY
B. WORTHY
C. LOWLY
D. LAUDABLE
E. COMPLIMENTARY
F. FROTHY

15

16

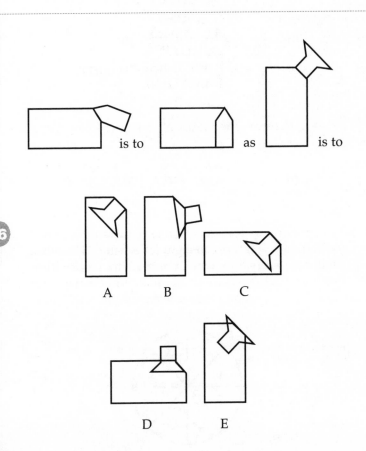

What is the group noun for a number of LEOPARDS?

A. CHIP
B. HUNT
C. STRIDE
D. PACK
E. LEPE

What two words are synonymous?

A. JAUNT
B. JUMP
C. INSULT
D. OUTING
E. PROMISE
F. IMAGINE

Place two three-letter segments together to form an extinct animal.

MBO STU AFE GGA GIR QUA

If the missing letters in the circle below are correctly inserted they will form an eight-letter word. The word will not necessarily have to be read in a clockwise direction, but the letters are in order. What is the word and missing letters?

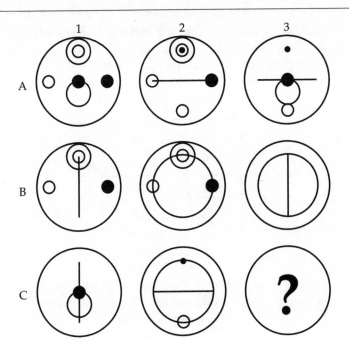

Which of the circles below should replace the
question mark above?

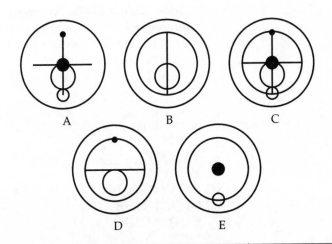

If the missing letters in the two circles below are correctly inserted they will form synonymous words. The words do not necessarily have to be read in a clockwise direction, but the letters are in order. What are the words and missing letters?

A word can be placed in the brackets that has the same meaning as the words outside. What is it? Each dot represents a letter.

A TYPE OF TREE (• • • •) YEARN

Find a six-letter word made up of only the following four letters?

**S H
A R**

What word is an antonym of LIEGE?

**A. LORD
B. VASSAL
C. SOVEREIGN
D. FORTRESS
E. NUNCIO**

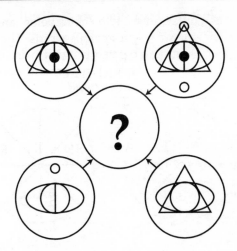

26

Each line and symbol that appears in the four outer circles, above, is transferred to the middle circle according to how many times it appears, as follows:

One time — it is transferred
Two times — it is possibly transferred
Three times — it is transferred
Four times — it is not transferred

Which of the options below should appear as the middle circle?

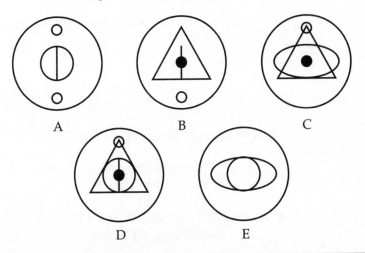

A   B   C

D   E

27

What word is a synonym of NUBILE?

A. LITHE
B. MARRIAGEABLE
C. INEBRIATED
D. LISSOM
E. SUPPLE

28

What word can be placed in front of the other five to form five new words or phrases? Each dot represents a letter.

(• • • •) ⟨

BALL
WAY
LAND
FLIER
BROW

29

If the missing letter in the circle below is correctly inserted it will form an eight-letter word. The word will not necessarily have to be read in a clockwise direction, but the letters are in order. What is the word and missing letter?

30

What is a SHADOOF?

A. A SHADOWY FIGURE
B. A RESERVOIR
C. A DAM
D. A WATER-RAISING CONTRAPTION
E. A RUNNING STREAM

Answers

Test **Four**

1

B.

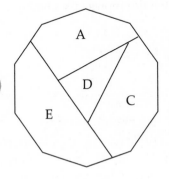

2

A.
Different symbols in adjoining circles on the same row are carried into the circle between them in the row above. Similar symbols in the same place are dropped.

3

Standard and ordinary. The missing letters are N and D (standard) and D and Y (ordinary).

4

183. 2197 ÷ 13 = 169.
The 169 candle stubs can be reused, so 169 ÷ 13 = 13 and 13 ÷ 13 = 1.
Therefore 169 + 13 + 1 = 183.

5

E (wink : nictitate).

6

B.
The two innermost segments both rotate 90° clockwise.

7

18.
In each column (top ÷ bottom) x 5 = middle. (54 ÷ 18)
[3] x 5 = 15.
Others are (18 ÷ 6)
[3] x 5 =15;
(24 ÷ 3) [8] x 5 = 40.

8

A (salubrious) and F (noxious).

9

Elephant. The others can all be prefixed by black; elephant can only be prefixed by white.

10 E (8795 : 1514 : 65).
The sum of the first two digits and the sum of the last two digits are put together and the process is repeated.

11 A.

12 C (chop).
A cleaver chops as a knife cuts.

13 B (over).
All the words can be prefixed by pass to make new words.

14 C (50 minutes).
The game lasts 75 minutes and 12 players can be in the game for its duration, so there are a total of 900 player minutes (75 minutes x 12 players) If 18 players are involved, the sum is (75 x 12) [900] ÷ 18 = 50.

15 B (worthy) and D (laudable).

16 A.
The top figure is folded along its adjoining line and moves into the lower one.

17 E (lepe).

18 A (jaunt) and D (outing).

19 Quagga.

20 Outhouse.
The missing letters are O and H.

21 C.
Reading across columns and down rows, unique elements in the first two are transferred to the third (bottom or right). Common elements disappear.

22 Impolite and insolent.
The missing letters are M (impolite) and L and T (insolent).

23 Pine.

24 Harass, Sahara, asharh (the 3rd month of the Bengali calendar), or hassar, a type of catfish.

25 B (vassal).

26 B.

27 B (marriageable).

28 High.

29 Hireling.
The missing letter is H.

30 D (a water-raising contraption).

Four of the five pieces below can be fitted together to form a perfect square. Which is the odd one out?

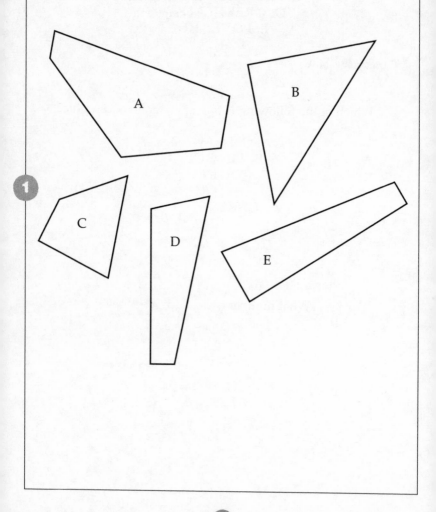

PHILANDER : FLIRT

Which pair of words below have the same relationship as the words above?

A. OBTAIN : FIND
B. MISTRUST : MISTREAT
C. PROSAIC : UNUSUAL
D. GREET : AFFIRM
E. LOVE : HUG

Which of the following is not an anagram of a reptile?

A. ON CANADA
B. TIN ROOM
C. COOL CIDER
D. CAROB
E. BIT HAUL

What number is the odd one out?

A. 36119
B. 22515
C. 57624
D. 28918
E. 90030

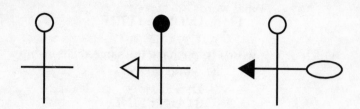

Which of the figures below will continue
the sequence above?

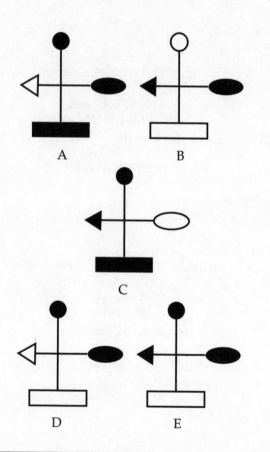

5

What words are antonymous?

A. CHANGE
B. ADMIRE
C. SOOTHE
D. STIR
E. VEX
F. EXPAND

6

Which of the following is the odd one out?

A. FEMUR
B. PATELLA
C. FIBULA
D. ULNA
E. TIBIA

7

What number should replace the question mark?

8

100   99.5   98.5   97   95   ?

Complete the two words using the letters of the following once only.
IDLING TURN

9

• A • • T • E •   • A • • T • E •

CRISIS (PRAISE) SPREAD

Following the same rules as above, what word should go in the brackets?

10

REPOSE (• • • • • •) ARENAS

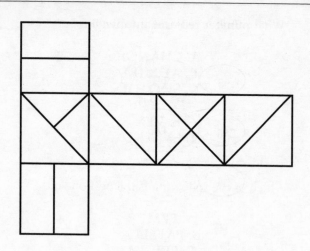

When the above is folded to form a cube, one of the figures below can be produced. What is it?

11

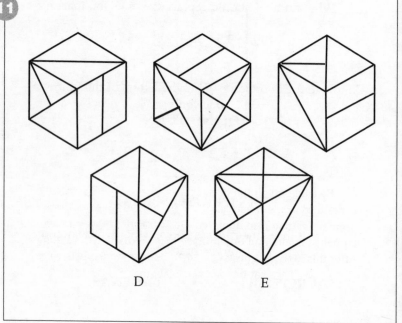

D   E

What number replaces the question mark?

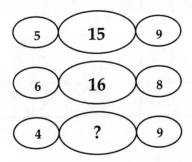

Start at a corner square and move in a clockwise spiral to the middle to spell out a nine-letter word. What are the missing letters?

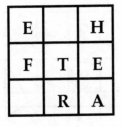

E		H
F	T	E
	R	A

By 8.00 pm, all the guests had arrived. By 8.30 pm, one-third of them had left. By 9.30 pm, one-third of those remaining had also departed. By 11.00 pm, the same had happened again, and one-third of those remaining had gone. After this, only 16 guests remained. How many guests were at the party at 8.00 pm?

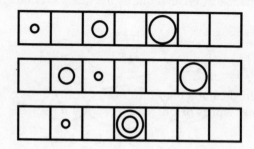

What should continue the sequence above?

15

A

B

C

D

E

Find a six-letter word made up of only the following four letters?

E L
T Y

What word can be placed in front of the other five to form five new words or phrases? Each dot represents a letter.

(• • • • •) ⟨ UP
TRIP
ABOUT
SHOULDERED
NUMBER

What number should replace the question mark?

119 108 99 81 72 ?

A. 63
B. 64
C. 65
D. 66
E. 67

If the missing letters in the circle below are correctly inserted they will form an eight-letter word. The word will not necessarily have to be read in a clockwise direction, but the letters are in order. What is the word and missing letters?

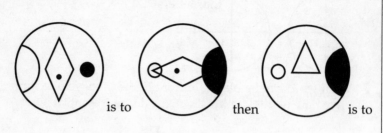

is to ... then ... is to

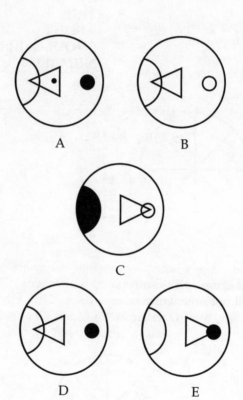

20

A

B

C

D

E

21

What number should replace the question mark?

If the missing letters in the two circles below are correctly
inserted they will form synonymous words. The words do
not necessarily have to be read in a clockwise direction,
but the letters are in order. What are the words and
missing letters?

22

A word can be placed in the brackets that has the same
meaning as the words outside. What is it? Each dot
represents a letter.

23

HORSE TACK (• • • • • • • • • • •)
A BETTING SYSTEM

Place two three-letter segments together to form a fish.

24

ENT   LET   PIK   MUL   GER   PAR

Which of the following is the odd one out?

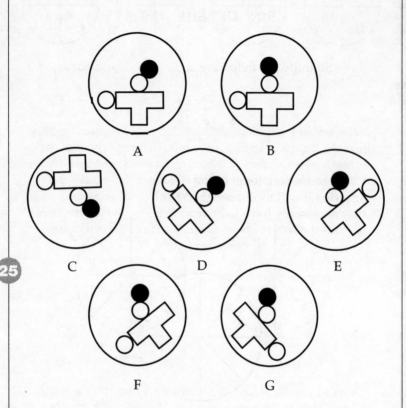

A

B

C

D

E

F

G

If one letter in each of the four words below is changed, a phrase can be found. What is it?

SIN OF SHE HENCE

Simplify the following and find the value of x.

$$\frac{5}{8} \div \frac{7}{16} \div \frac{10}{14} = x$$

If the missing letter in the circle below is correctly inserted it will form an eight-letter word. The word will not necessarily have to be read in a clockwise direction, but the letters are in order. What is the word and missing letter?

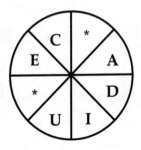

What word is a synonym of JOCOSE?

A. MISERLY
B. MISERABLE
C. CHEERFUL
D. GENEROUS
E. IMPARTIAL

Which of the hexagons at the bottom should replace the question mark below?

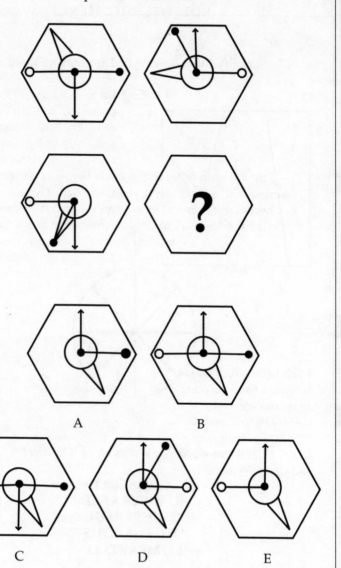

Answers

1

D.

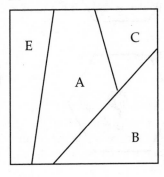

2

E (love : hug).

3

E (bit haul) which makes halibut, a fish. The other anagrams are: ON CANADA (anaconda), TIN ROOM (monitor), COOL CIDER (crocodile), and CAROB (cobra).

4

D (28918).
The first three digits of the other numbers is the square of the last two digits: 361 is the square of 19, 225 is the square of 15, 576 is the square of 24, and 900 is the square of 30.

5

D.
A new and different white symbol is added to one of the arms at each stage. The symbol then alternates between black and white at each stage.

6

C (soothe) and E (vex).

7

D (ulna, a bone in a human's arm). The others are bones in a human's leg.

8

92.5.
At each stage the numbers reduce by 0.5, 1, 1.5, 2, and 2.5, respectively.

9 Gauntlet and daintier.

10. Reason.
Three letters of the left and right words transfer to the middle as follows:

R	E	P	O	S	E
	2		5	4	
(R	E	A	S	O	N)
1	2	3	4	5	6
A	R	E	N	A	S
	1		6	3	

11 D.

12. In each case the sum is (left x right) ÷ 3 = middle.
(4 x 9) [36] ÷ 3 = 12.
The others are: (5 x 9) [45] ÷ 3 = 15;
(6 x 8) [48] ÷ 3 = 16.

13 Heartfelt.
The missing letters are T and L.

14 54 guests at 8.00 pm.

D.
At each stage, the small circle moves two squares right and one left; the medium circle moves one left and two right; and the large circle moves one right and two left.

16 Eyelet or Tetley, a brand of tea.

17 Round.

18 A (63). The sum of digits is removed from the first number to create the second and the sequence continues.
72 – 7 – 2 = 63.
The sequence starts:
119 – 1 – 1 – 9 = 108;
108 – 1 – 8 = 99;
99 – 9 – 9 = 81;
81 – 8 – 1 = 72.

19 Objector.
The missing letters are J and T.

E.
The middle figure rotates 90° clockwise and the outer figures rotate 180° and change from black to white and vice versa.

4.
In each case the sums of the numbers in diagonally opposite sectors are the same.

21

22
Increase and heighten. The missing letters are C and S (increase) and H twice (heighten).

23
Martingale.

24
Mullet.

25
E.
The others all have identical pairs in different rotations: A and F, B and D, and C and G.

26
Sit on the fence.

2.
The sum can expressed as:
$$\frac{5}{8} \times \frac{16}{7} \times \frac{14}{10} = 2.$$

27

28
Guidance.
The missing letters are G and N.

29
C (cheerful).

30
A. In each case, the white circle and black arrow both rotate 180°, the white arrow rotates 60° anti- (counter) clockwise, and the black dot rotates 120° anti- (counter) clockwise.

Which three of the five pieces below can be fitted together to form an image of a cuboid?

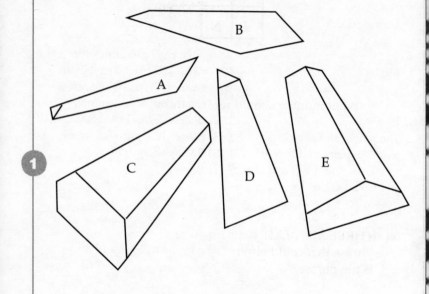

A. ACD
B. ABC
C. CDE
D. BCD
E. ADE

Find the starting point and move from square to adjoining square, horizontally or vertically, but not diagonally, to spell a 12-letter word, using each letter once only. What are the missing letters?

R	A	
	A	M
S	S	E
I	N	

What number should replace the question mark?

53 (3) 59
71 (8) 78
29 (?) 98

THREE MEN EXIT is an anagram of a three-word phrase that could also be "the highest degree". What is the phrase?

Find two words with different spellings, but which sound alike, that can mean:

SKIN / HURRIED

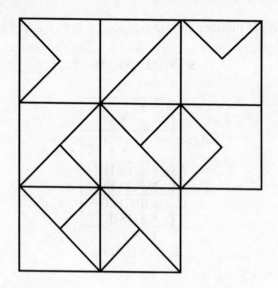

Which of the squares below should go in the blank space above?

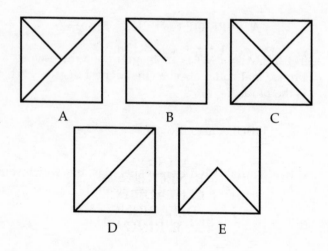

A   B   C

D   E

What number should replace the question mark?

3 9 11 33 35 ?

What two words are antonymous?

**A. REFRESHING
B. INVITING
C. DELIGHTFUL
D. SENSIBLE
E. WISE
F. INVIDIOUS**

A word can be placed in the brackets that has the same meaning as the words outside. What is it? Each dot represents a letter.

A TYPE OF GREEK GODDESS
(• • • •) PONDER

FIBULA is to BROOCH as TORC is to?

**A. CROWN
B. NECKBAND
C. HEADPIECE
D. EARRING
E. RING**

11

What two words are synonymous?

A. BAN
B. BANAL
C. FIT
D. HOLD
E. PERMIT
F. PROSCRIBE

12

What positive number replaces the question mark?

2	4	2
16	12	48
8	12	?

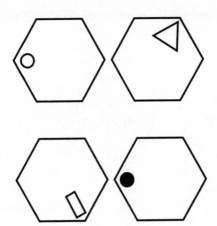

13 Which of the hexagons below will continue
the above sequence?

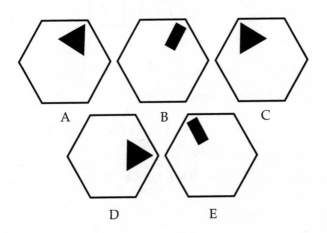

A   B   C

D   E

What number replaces the question mark?

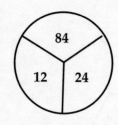 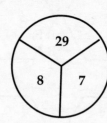 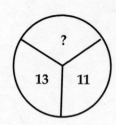

What word is the odd one out?

A. PEDIGREE
B. SPECIES
C. BREED
D. STRIPE
E. STRAIN

What is the essential ingredient of SAUERKRAUT?

A. PEPPERS
B. CHEESE
C. SQUID
D. SAUSAGE
E. CABBAGE

Find a six-letter word made up of only the
following four letters?

17

L E
B P

What word can be placed in front of the other five to
form five new words? Each dot represents a letter.

18

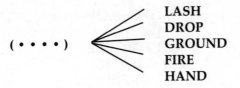

(• • • •)   **LASH**
DROP
GROUND
FIRE
HAND

If the missing letters in the circle below are correctly
inserted they will form an eight-letter word. The word
will not necessarily have to be read in a clockwise
direction, but the letters are in order. What is the word
and missing letters?

19

Which of the following is the odd one out?

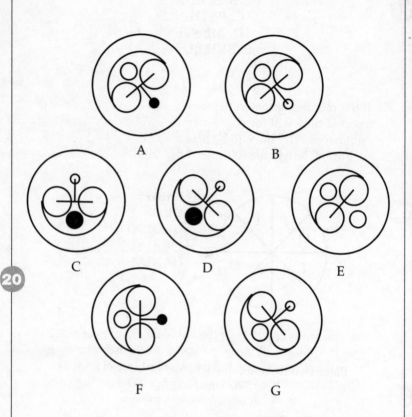

What word has the same meaning as ECLAT?

A. JEALOUSY
B. SORDID
C. PATIENCE
D. MYSTERY
E. BRILLIANCE

If the missing letters in the two circles below are correctly inserted they will form synonymous words. The words do not necessarily have to be read in a clockwise direction, but the letters are in order. What are the words and missing letters?

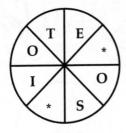 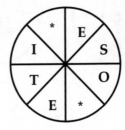

Place two three-letter segments together to form a nautical item.

SER   FUN   GUN   VAN   ELS   HAW

A word can be placed in the brackets that has the same meaning as the words outside. What is it? Each dot represents a letter.

MOVE ON ITS AXIS (• • •)
COOKING UTENSIL

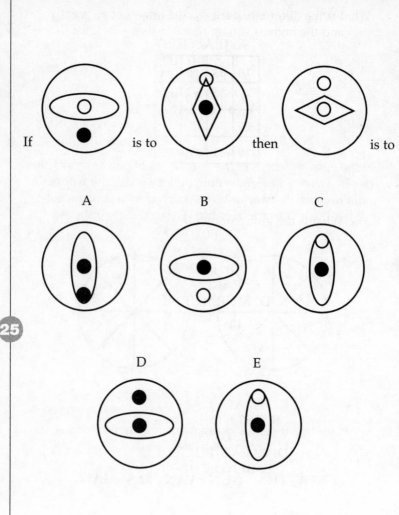

If ⬡ is to ⬡ then ⬡ is to

A   B   C

D   E

What is the difference between the lowest cube number
and the highest square number shown below?

10	17	80	41
36	16	10	26
25	14	7	8
19	11	190	23

What is the group noun for a number of OWLS?

A. GAGGLE
B. FLOCK
C. PARLIAMENT
D. MURMURATION
E. FLIGHT

What is a synonym of GENUFLECT?

A. ACCENTUATE
B. BREATHE HEAVILY
C. GIVE WAY
D. CLEAR THE THROAT
E. BEND THE KNEE

Which two words are antonymous?

A. ENTANGLE
B. COVERT
C. ASSUAGE
D. IRRITATE
E. BRANDISH

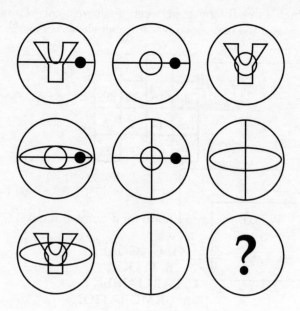

30

Which of the circles above should replace the
question mark below?

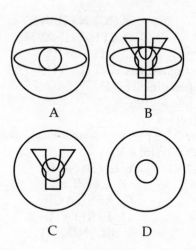

A

B

C

D

Answers

A (ACD).

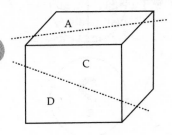

1

2 Embarrassing.
The missing letters are, reading from top to bottom, B, R and G.

3 4.
The sums are: (right digits multiplied) ÷ (left digits multiplied) = middle. (9×8) $[72] ÷ (2 \times 9) [18] = 4$.
The others are:
$(5 \times 9) [45] ÷ (5 \times 3) [15] = 3$;
$(7 \times 8) [56] ÷ (7 \times 1) [7] = 8$.

4 In the extreme.

5 Hide and hied.

6 D.
Reading across columns and down rows, unique elements in the first two squares are transferred to the third (bottom or right). Common elements disappear.

7 105.
The sequence alternates:
x3, +2. $3 \times 3 = 9$;
$9 + 2 = 11$; $11 \times 3 = 33$;
$33 + 2 = 35$; $35 \times 3 = 105$.

8 C (delightful) and F (invidious).

9 Muse.

10 B (neckband).

11 A (ban) and F (proscribe).

12

24.
In each row (left x middle) ÷ 4 = right. (8 x 12) [96] ÷ 4 = 24.
The others are: (2 x 4) [8] ÷ 4 = 2; (16 x 12) [192] ÷ 4 = 48.

13

A.
The figures rotate 120° clockwise and the circle, triangle, and rectangle are white first time, black second time.

14

46.
The sums are: (top − left) ÷ 3 = right.
(46 − 13) [33] ÷ 3 = 11.
The others are:
(84 − 12) [72] ÷ 3 = 24;
(29 − 8) [21] ÷ 3 = 7.

15

B (species, a general word). The others are types of species.

16

E (cabbage).

17

Pebble.

18

Back.

19

Outshone.
The missing letters are O and H.

20

E. The others are all pairs in different rotations, A and F, B and G, and C and D.

21

E (brilliance).

22

Toilsome and tiresome.
The missing letters are L and M (toilsome) and R and M (tiresome).

23

Hawser.

24

Pan.

25

A.
The oval becomes a diamond and vice versa, and rotates 90° clockwise. The circles change from black to white and vice versa, and rotate 180°.

26 28.
The lowest cube number is 8, the highest square number is 36; 36 − 8 = 28.

27 C (parliament).

28 E (bend the knee).

29 C and D (assuage and irritate).

30 B.
Reading across columns and down rows, unique elements in the first two circles are transferred to the third (bottom or right). Common elements disappear.

Which three of the five pieces below can be fitted together
to form a perfect square?

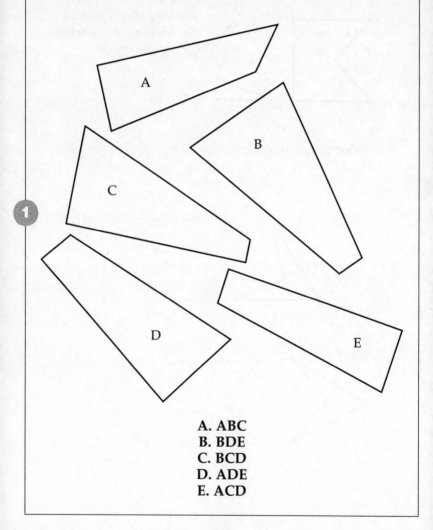

A. ABC
B. BDE
C. BCD
D. ADE
E. ACD

328

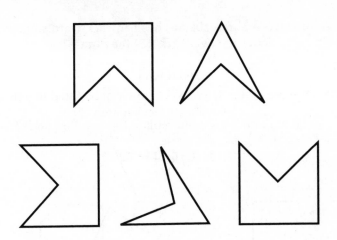

What option below continues the above sequence?

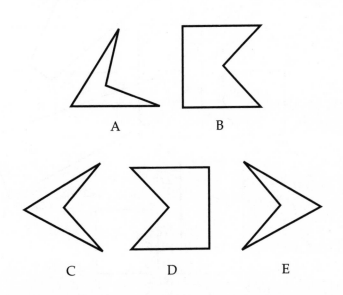

A

B

C

D

E

3 A three-word phrase, below, has had each word's initial letter removed. What is the phrase?

IRDFREY

4 What number should replace the question mark?

0 1 5 14 30 ?

is to as is to

A   B   C

D   E

To which square from the five at the bottom can a dot be added so that it meets the same conditions as the box below?

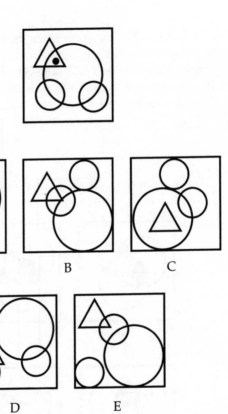

A

B

C

D

E

7

If one letter in each of the four words below is changed, a phrase can be found. What is it?

TALE FAR I RUDE

8

A train, 0.25 miles long, going at a speed of 40mph enters a tunnel that is 2.25 miles long. How long does it take for all of the train to pass through the tunnel from the moment the front enters it, to the moment the rear emerges?

9

Which of the following is the odd one out?

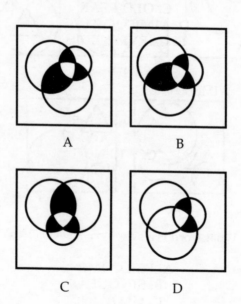

A   B

C   D

Start at a corner square and move in a clockwise spiral to the middle to spell out a nine-letter word. What are the missing letters?

T	E	R
	D	E
E		F

Which of the following is not an anagram of a form of transport?

A. RAIL REIN
B. NOD GOAL
C. OLD PEAR
D. AIM LOO TUBE
E. CARVE FORTH

WIMBLE is to DRILL as ROUTER is to?

A. HAMMER
B. SHAPE
C. WRENCH
D. HIT
E. CUT

What word is a synonym of SALUTARY?

A. WELCOMING
B. SINGULAR
C. GLOWING
D. CRINGING
E. BENEFICIAL

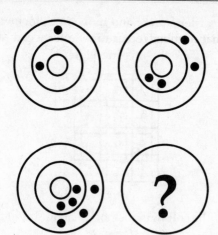

What figure below continues the sequence above?

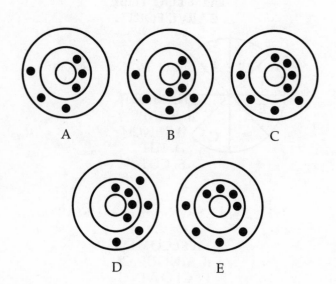

What number replaces the question mark?

7	3	4	8
9	11	?	5
6	9	4	1
4	1	1	4

If the missing letters in the two circles below are correctly inserted they will form synonymous words. The words do not necessarily have to be read in a clockwise direction, but the letters are in order. What are the words and missing letters?

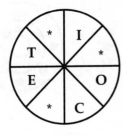

Find a six-letter word made up of only the following four letters?

L B
F E

Place two three-letter segments to form a bird?

RAN LEW ROW TIT CUR SPA

What word can be placed in front of the other five to form five new words? Each dot represents a letter.

(• • • •)

TIME
MOON
PAY
TRUTH
WAY

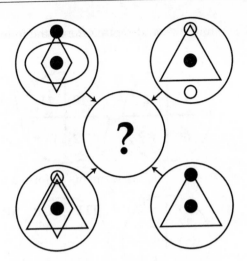

Each line and symbol that appears in the four outer circles, above, is transferred to the middle circle according to how many times it appears, as follows:

One time — it is transferred
Two times — it is possibly transferred
Three times — it is transferred
Four times — it is not transferred

Which of the circles below should appear in the middle circle?

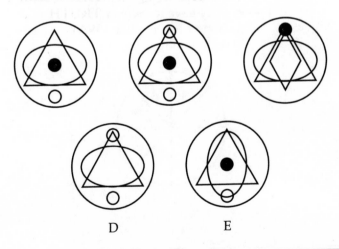

D   E

What number should replace the question mark?

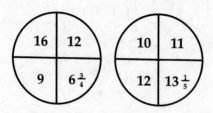

If the missing letters in the circle below are correctly inserted they will form an eight-letter word. The word will not necessarily have to be read in a clockwise direction, but the letters are in order. What is the word and missing letters?

338

23 Which word is a synonym of SPINDRIFT?

A. FLOTSAM
B. SEA-SPRAY
C. SPINNAKER
D. TOPSAIL
E. RUDDER-BEARING

---

24 A word can be placed in the brackets that has the same meaning as the words outside. What is it? Each dot represents a letter.

BASKET (• • • • • •) IMPEDE

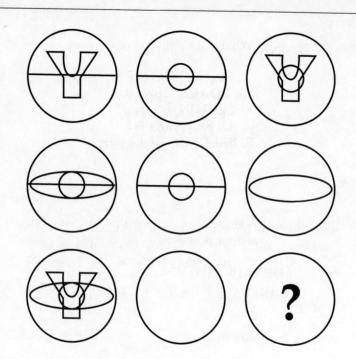

What circle should replace the question mark?

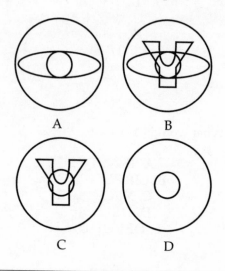

A B

C D

What is a CARBONADE?

26

A. NECKWEAR
B. POACHER'S GUN
C. CUT OF MEAT
D. SOFT DRINK
E. BELT FOR BULLETS

27

Place three two-letter segments together to form another word for nonsense or deception.

DE MB SW UG IN HU DL

What is the group noun for a number of PARTRIDGES?

28

A. COVEY
B. SEDGE
C. WEDGE
D. FLOCK
E. DRIFT

What word is a synonym of EXIGENCY?

29

A. INNUENDO
B. CIRCUITOUSLY
C. NECESSITY
D. DELUSION
E. DEVOUTNESS

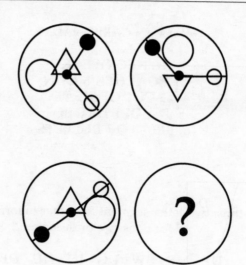

What circle will continue the sequence?

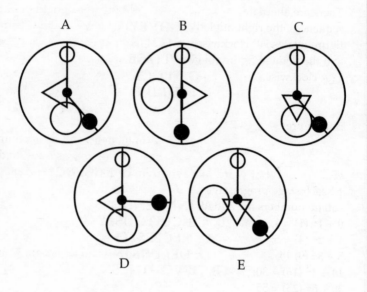

30

A   B   C

D   E

Answers

Test Twelve

1 B (BDE).

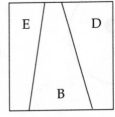

2 A.
There are alternate sequences, the right-angled figure rotates 90° clockwise, and the pointed figure rotates 120° clockwise.

3 Bird of prey.

4 55.
At each stage progressive square numbers are added.
$0 + 1^2 (1) = 1$;
$1 + 2^2 (4) = 5$;
$5 + 3^2 (9) 14$;
$14 + 4^2 (16) = 30$;
$30 + 5^2 (25) = 55$.

5 A.
The top half is folded across the middle and placed over the bottom half.

6 C.
The dot appears in the large circle and the triangle.

7 Take for a ride.

8 3 minutes, 45 seconds.
Add the train length (0.25m) to the tunnel length (2.25m) and multiply by the number of minutes per mile covered ($^{60}/40$, or 1.5). $2.5 \times 1.5 = 3.75$.

9 D.
In the others all areas common to only two circles are shaded. In D, one such area is not covered.

10 Reflected.
The missing letters are L and C.

C (OLD PEAR or leopard).
The others are:
RAIL REIN (airliner),
NOD GOAL (gondola),
AIM LOO TUBE
(automobile), and CARVE
FORTH (hovercraft).

11

12 E (cut).

13 E (beneficial).

14
C.
At each stage two dots are
added; outer dots rotate 45°
clockwise; inner dots rotate
45° anti- (counter) clockwise.

15
7.
The sums are: (first
column + third column) =
(second column + fourth
column). $(9 + 7) = (11 + 5)$.
The others are:
$(7 + 4) = (3 + 8)$;
$(6 + 4) = (9 + 1)$;
$(4 + 1) = (1 + 4)$.

16
Ricochet and bouncing.
The missing letters are R,
C and H (ricochet) and B
and N (bouncing).

17 Feeble or befell.

18 Curlew.

19 Half.

20 D.

21
$8\frac{2}{3}$.
The sums are:
(bottom left x top right) =
(top left x bottom right).
$(13 \times 4)\ [52] = (6 \times 8\frac{2}{3})\ [52]$.
The others are:
$(9 \times 12)\ [108] \times (16 \times 6\frac{3}{4})$
$[108]$;
$(12 \times 11)\ [132] = (10 \times 13\frac{1}{5})$
$[132]$;
$(9 \times 7)\ [63] \times (12 \times 5\frac{1}{4})\ [63]$.

22
Upstairs.
The missing letters are U and
A.

23 B (sea-spray).

24 Hamper.

B.

Reading across columns and down rows, unique elements in the first two circles are transferred to the third (bottom or right). Common elements disappear.

26 C (cut of meat, specifically a chop).

27 Humbug.

28 A (covey).

29 C (necessity).

C.

At each stage the triangle rotates 180°, the large circle rotates 90° clockwise, the small white circle rotates 45° anti- (counter) clockwise, and the small black circle rotates 90° anti- (counter) clockwise.

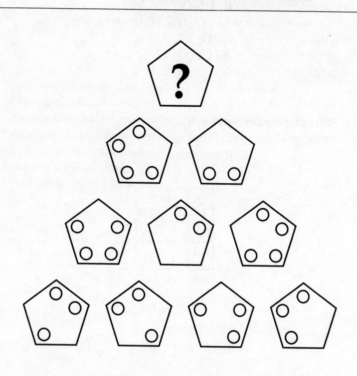

Which of the pentagons below should replace the question mark?

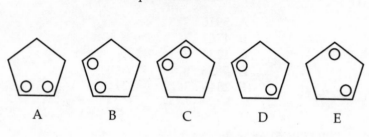

A   B   C   D   E

What word is a synonym of GENERIC?

A. PRECISE
B. UNIVERSAL
C. OLD
D. WEAK
E. COMPLETE

Start at a corner square and move in a clockwise spiral to the middle to spell out a nine-letter word. What are the missing letters?

	O	
A	L	A
C	I	N

4627 : 6445 : 8263

Which series below has the same relationship as the series above?

A. 5916 : 7734 : 9552
B. 4763 : 3854 : 2945
C. 1234 : 3214 : 4123
D. 7856 : 6947 : 4769
E. 2846 : 5971 : 8352

EPIC PROSE is an anagram of what nine-letter word?

Which of the following pentagons in the odd one out?

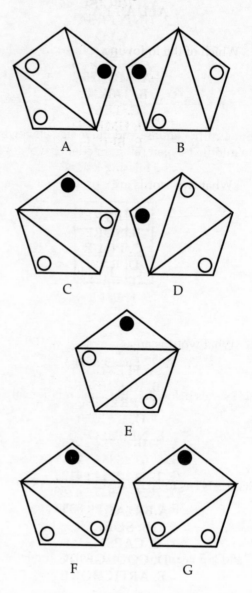

A

B

C

D

E

F

G

7

If one letter in each of the three words below is changed, a phrase can be found. What is it?

ALL AS BASE

8

Which of the following is the odd one out?

A. MOCHA
B. TAWNY
C. TEAL
D. UMBER
E. BEIGE

9

What two words are closest in meaning?

A. PURE
B. SORE
C. POUR
D. RAW
E. SAD
F. VILE

10

What word is an antonym of WOOLLY?

A. FLEXIBLE
B. REGULAR
C. PRECISE
D. RARE
E. NEBULOUS

11

EGGPLANT is to AUBERGINE as ZUCCHINI is to?

A.BREADFRUIT
B. SORREL
C. CAPSICUM
D. COURGETTE
E. ARTICHOKE

Which three of the five pieces below can be fitted together to form a perfect square?

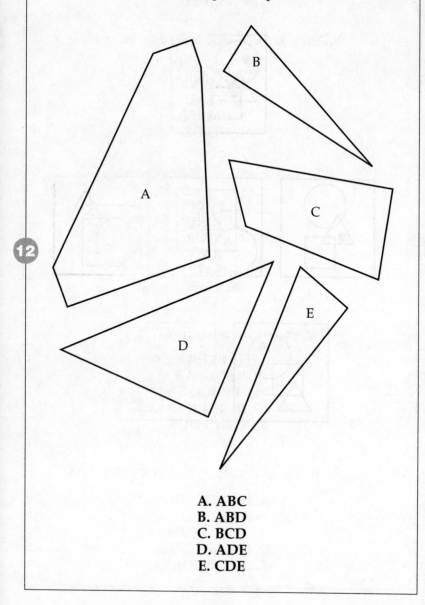

A. ABC
B. ABD
C. BCD
D. ADE
E. CDE

To which square at the bottom, A, B, C, D, or E, can a dot be added so that it meets the conditions in the box above them?

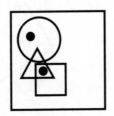

A

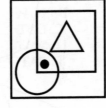

B

C

D

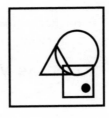

E

Find two words with different spellings, but sound
alike, that can mean:

WAN / BUCKET

What word goes with the following?

RED KING TAN

A. LET
B. ROW
C. CAT
D. MAT
E. PAT

Place three two-letter segments together to form a word
for a system of magic.

RO OD AS VO ST OO LO

What number should replace the question mark?

17

6 7 2 9 –2 11 ?

A word can be placed in the brackets that has the same meaning as the words outside. What is it? Each dot represents a letter.

18

POST (• • • • •) ANTE

If the missing letters in the circle below are correctly inserted they will form an eight-letter word. The word will not necessarily have to be read in a clockwise direction, but the letters are in order. What is the word and missing letters?

19

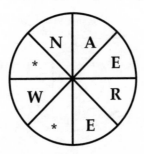

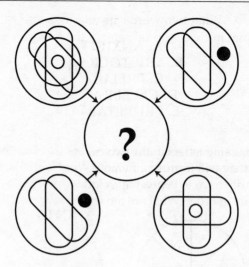

Each line and symbol that appears in the four outer circles, above, is transferred to the middle circle according to how many times it appears, as follows:

One time — it is transferred
Two times — it is possibly transferred
Three times — it is transferred
Four times — it is not transferred

Which of the circles below should appear as the middle circle?

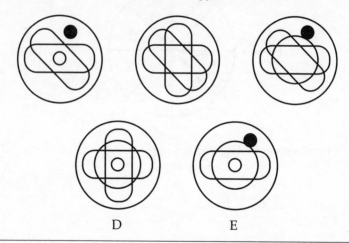

D   E

What two words are antonymous?

A. ANXIETY
B. ARISTOCRACY
C. PRELUDE
D. CELEBRATED
E. PROLETARIAT

If the missing letters in the two circles below are correctly inserted they will form synonymous words. The words do not necessarily have to be read in a clockwise direction, but the letters are in order. What are the words and missing letters?

What word can be placed in front of the other five to form five new words? Each dot represents a letter.

(• • •)

NOT
TEEN
NON
TON
DID

Find a six-letter word made up of only the following four letters?

H E
C R

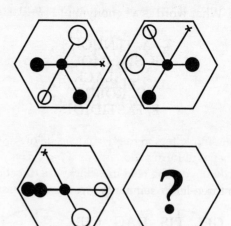

Which of the hexagons below should replace
the question mark above?

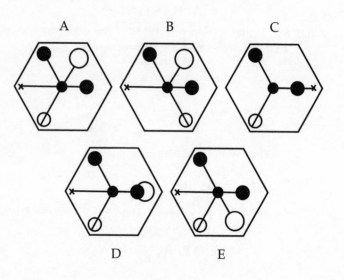

A   B   C

D   E

What word is a synonym of FLACCID?

A. TENUOUS
B. SPASMODIC
C. SLACK
D. ROBUST
E. FASTIDIOUS

26

Place two three-letter segments together to form a weapon.

GEL   PIS   DAG   CUD   TLE   GIT

27

What is the group noun given to a number of BAKERS?

A. HASTINESS
B. SUBTLETY
C. CONGREGATION
D. RISING
E. TABERNACLE

28

What word is the antonym of LACONIC?

A. SENTENTIOUS
B. SUCCINCT
C. LOQUACIOUS
D. SCANTINESS
E. APPREHENSIVE

29

Each of the nine squares in the grid marked 1A to 3C should incorporate all of the items which are shown in the squares of the same letter and number, at the left and top, respectively. For example, 2B should incorporate all of the symbols that are in squares 2 and B. One square, however, is incorrect. Which one is it?

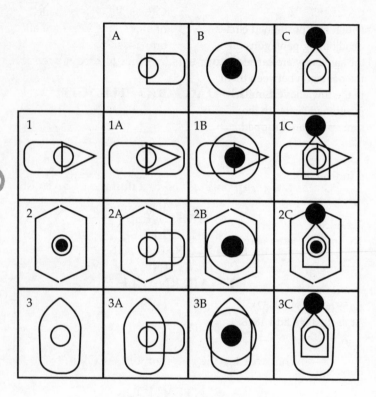

Answers

1 C.
Differently positioned circles in adjoining pentagons on the same row are carried into the pentagon between them in the row above. Similarly positioned circles in the same place are dropped.

2 B (universal).

3 Botanical.
The missing letters are B and T.

4 A (5916 : 7734 : 9552).
At each stage add 1818.

5 Periscope.

6 F.
The others all have identical pairs in different rotations, A and G, B and E, and C and D.

7 Ill at ease.

8 C (teal, which is a shade of blue). The others are all brownish shades.

9 B (sore) and D (raw).

10 C (precise).

11 D (courgette).
It is another name for the vegetable.

12 B (ABD).

13

D.
The second dot appears in the link between the triangle and the square.

14

Pale and pail.

15

B (row).
The words can all be prefixed by SPAR, to make sparrow, sparred, sparking, spartan.

16

Voodoo.

17

–6.
There are alternate sequences,
– 4 and + 2.
The series are: 6, 2, –2, and –6, and 7, 9, and 11.

18

Stake.

19

Anywhere. The missing letters are Y and H.

20

C.

21

B (aristocracy) and E (proletariat).

22

Annoying and worrying. The missing letters are N and G (annoying) and W and Y (worrying).

23

Can.

24

Creche, creech (a pointed hill) or cheche, a Tuareg head scarf.

25

A.
At each stage the short-lined black circle rotates 180°, the small white circle rotates 120° clockwise, the long-lined black circle rotates 60° clockwise, the large circle rotates 120° anti- (counter) clockwise, and the cross rotates 60° anti- (counter) clockwise.

26

C (slack).

27

Cudgel.

28 E (tabernacle).

29 C (loquacious).

30 2A.

Find two synonymous words in the inner and outer spirals of the circle below, one reading clockwise, the other anti- (counter) clockwise. What are the words and missing letters ?

Complete the two words using the letters of the following once only.

FIND MRS BILGE

• • S • E • • E •   • • S • E • • E •

What number should continue the sequence and replace the question mark?

1 2 5 14 41 122 ?

What word is an antonym of PSEUDO?

A. NORMAL
B. ARTIFICIAL
C. PRUDENT
D. AUTHENTIC
E. PROVISION

Which of the following is the odd one out?

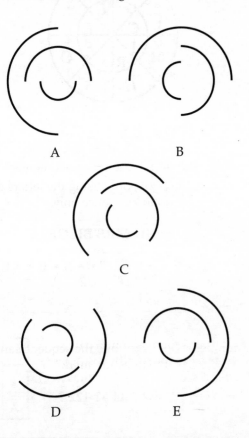

A   B

C

D   E

Which of the following is the odd one out?

A. GOAT
B. BULL
C. CHICKEN
D. LION
E. RAM

6

Complete the three-letter words which, reading down, will reveal an animal.

7

H	E	(•)
F	O	(•)
L	E	(•)
S	I	(•)
H	A	(•)
A	R	(•)
W	O	(•)
B	A	(•)

What number should replace the question mark?

9768 : 7488   3744 : ?

8

A. 2516
B. 2732
C. 2814
D. 2816
E. 2852

Start at a corner square and move in a clockwise spiral to the middle to spell out a nine-letter word. What are the missing letters?

9

U		S
T	E	I
A	N	

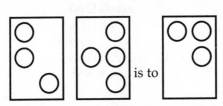

is to

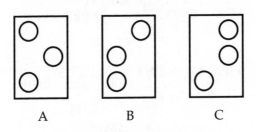

as

is to

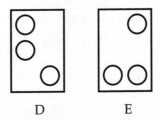

A   B   C

D   E

What word is a synonym of DISINTERESTED?

A. IMPARTIAL
B. STRONG
C. STAUNCH
D. IMPETURBABLE
E. ODD

11

EPISTLE : LETTER

Which pair of words below has the same relationship
as the pair above?

A. HOMILY : FAREWELL
B. ACRONYM : OPPOSITE
C. LEXICON : ORIGIN
D. EPITHET : NAME
E. SYNTAX : REVENUE

12

SUDDEN MOMENT TUMULT WEANING

What comes next?

A. CHARMING
B. PRECIPITATION
C. THEME
D. HARMONY
E. CONGRATULATE

13

If one letter in each of the three words below is changed,
a phrase can be found. What is it?

FIND ANY CANDY

14

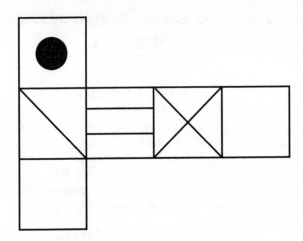

When the above is folded to form a cube, just one of the following can be produced. Which one is it?

15

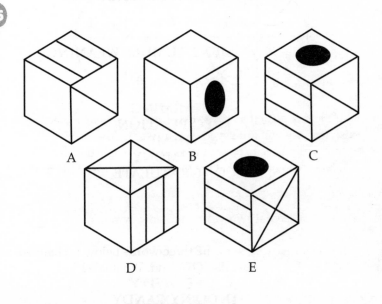

A B C

D E

367

Find a six-letter word made up of only the following four letters?

V O
L E

What word can be placed in front of the other five to form five new words? Each dot represents a letter.

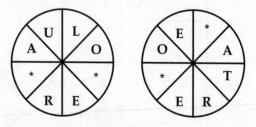

(• • • •)

TURN
STAIRS
POUR
RIGHT
FALL

If the missing letters in the two circles below are correctly inserted they will form synonymous words. The words do not necessarily have to be read in a clockwise direction, but the letters are in order. What are the words and missing letters?

What two words are antonymous?

A. SPIRITUAL
B. POLLUTED
C. DEPRAVITY
D. CORPOREAL
E. HARMONY

Each of the nine squares in the grid marked 1A to 3C should incorporate all of the items which are shown in the squares of the same letter and number, at the left and top, respectively. For example, 2B should incorporate all of the symbols that are in squares 2 and B. One square, however, is incorrect.

Which one is it?

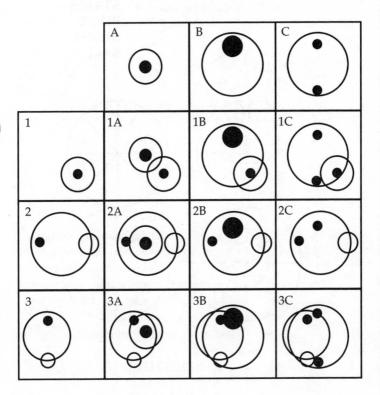

What word is a synonym of HUCKSTER?

A. MECHANIC
B. GAMBLER
C. PEDLAR
D. GIGOLO
E. SEAMSTRESS

What number should replace the question mark?

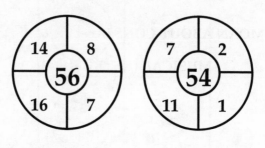

23

Place two three-letter segments together to form a boat.

TER MAS GAL IRE CUT EON

24

A word can be placed in the brackets that has the same meaning as the words outside. What is it? Each dot represents a letter.

MOAN ABOUT CONSTANTLY (• • • •)

MUSICAL INSTRUMENT

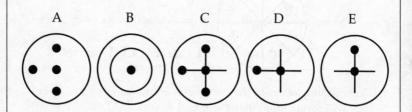

Which of the circles above should replace the
question mark below?

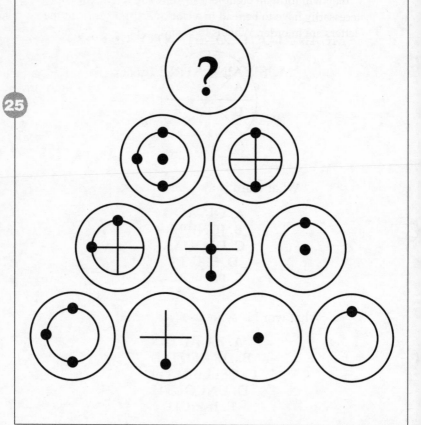

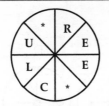 

26

If the missing letters in the two circles above are correctly inserted they will form antonymous words. The words do not necessarily have to be read in a clockwise direction, but the letters are in order. What are the words and missing letters?

If the missing letters in the circle below are correctly inserted they will form an eight-letter word. The word will not necessarily have to be read in a clockwise direction, but the letters are in order. What is the word and missing letters?

27

28

What word is the odd one out?

A. GINKGO
B. JUNIPER
C. DEODAR
D. SISKIN
E. PAWPAW

29

What word is synonym of DIFFIDENT?

A. BASHFUL
B. DEMENTED
C. CELEBRATED
D. UNCOUTH
E. ILLICIT

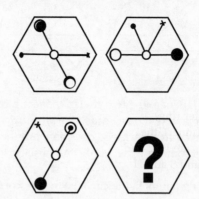

Which of the hexagons below should replace the question mark above?

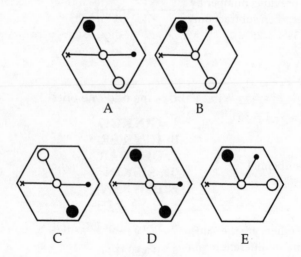

Answers

1 Opulence (outer ring) and richness (inner). the missing letters are P, L, and E (opulence) and S and H (richness).

2 Disbelief and messenger.

3 365. At each stage multiply the previous number by three, then subtract one.
1 x 3 - 1 = 2;
2 x 3 - 1 = 5;
5 x 3 - 1 = 14;
14 x 3 - 1 = 41;
41 x 3 - 1 = 122;
122 x 3 - 1 = 365.

4 D (authentic).

5 E.
The others are the same figure in different rotations.

6 C (chicken).
Rooster is an oriental astrological sign. The others are all western astrological signs (Capricorn – goat, Taurus – bull, Leo – lion, and Aries – ram).

7 Reindeer. The words are: heR, foE, leI, siN, haD, arE, woE, baR.

8 A (2516). The first and third digits and second and fourth digits are made into two, two-digit numbers and multiplied together.
96 x 78 = 7488;
78 x 48 = 3744;
34 x 74 = 2516.

9 Signature. The missing letters are G and R.

10 B. The circles in the two boxes are transferred to the third one only if they are not in similar positions. Similarly-placed circles disappear.

11 A. Impartial.

12 D (epithet : name).

13 C (theme).
The initial two letters of the words are the same as the days of the week.

14 Fine and dandy.

15 E.

16 Evolve or O-level, a British exam.

17 Down.

18 Overhaul and overtake. The missing letters are V and H (overhaul) and V and K (overtake).

19 A (spiritual) and D (corporeal).

20 2C.

21 C (pedlar).

22 64. In each case the sum is (top left – bottom right) x (bottom left – top right).
(26 – 18) [8] x (21 – 13) [8] = 64.

The others are:
(14 – 7) [7] x (16 – 8) [8] = 56;
(7 – 1) [6] x (11 – 2) [9] = 54;
(14 – 11) [3] x (17 – 8) [9] = 27.

23 Cutter.

24 Harp.

25 D.
Different symbols in adjoining circles on the same row are carried into the circle between them in the row above.
Similar symbols in the same place are dropped.

26 Cheerful and desolate.
The missing letters are H and F (cheerful) and D and L (desolate).

27 Piquancy.
The missing letters are Q and C.

28 D (siskin, a bird).
The others are trees.

29 A (bashful).

30 A.
At each stage the large circles both rotate 120° clockwise, the dot rotates 60° clockwise, and the cross rotates 60° anti-(counter) clockwise.

Test **Bonanza**

Place four of the three-letter segments together to form two synonymous words?

1

HEW	INT	ETH	EST	ICS	NIC	ION
ONE	HID	IVE	STR	MOT	NAT	ESC

AGLOW   ENVY   GHOST   HINT   ?

Which one of the words below should replace the question mark above?

2

A. CALM
B. ANNOY
C. HOPE
D. FIST
E. MAKE

3

What number should replace the question mark?

13   44   88   176   847   ?

What which of the following words in the odd one out?

4

A. DULCET
B. SOFT
C. MELODIC
D. EUPHONIOUS
E. HARMONIOUS

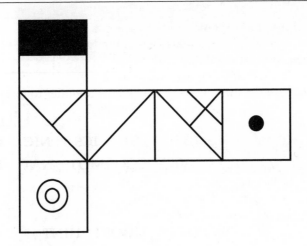

When the above is folded to form a cube, only one of the following can be produced. What one is it?

5

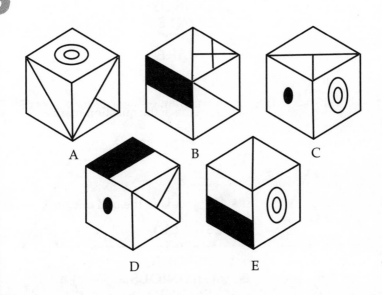

A

B

C

D

E

Find the starting point and move from square to adjoining square, horizontally or vertically, but not diagonally, to spell a 12-letter word, using each letter once only. What are the missing letters?

I		U
N	A	L
A		I
M	E	

Which of the following is the odd one out?

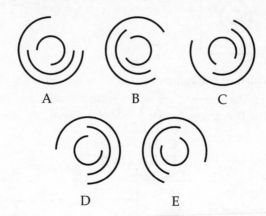

DEMONIC VIPER is an anagram of what 12-letter word?

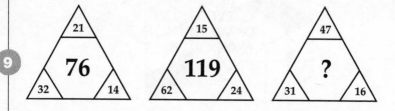

What number should replace the question mark?

Take one letter from each of the synonyms below, in order, to spell out another synonym of the keyword.

KEYWORD: **VALOROUS**

SYNONYMS: **STOUTHEARTED**
FEARLESS
INTREPID
DOUGHTY
VALIANT
COURAGEOUS

Which of the following words is the odd one out?

A. LARGE
B. BROAD
C. PERVASIVE
D. SWEEPING
E. WIDESPREAD

CLAVIER is to PIANO as TAMBOUR is to:

A. PERCUSSION
B. DRUM
C. XYLOPHONE
D. ACCORDION
E. WOODWIND

13

What number should replace the question mark?

1.5   0.5   3.5   10.5   7.5   2.5   ?

14

A word can be placed in the brackets to go at the end of the left word and the start of the right word, creating two new words. Each dot represents a letter. What are the three words?

OFF   (• • •)   ANGER

15

If a car had increased its average speed for a 180-mile journey by 5 mph, the journey would have been completed in 30 minutes less. What was the car's original average speed?

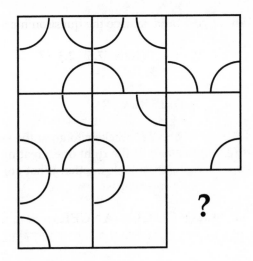

16

Which is of the squares below will replace the question mark above?

A   B   C   D

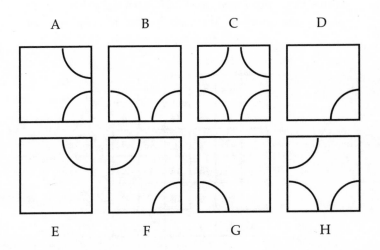

E   F   G   H

What two words are opposite in meaning?

A. WORRIED
B. PIOUS
C. ANGRY
D. IRREVERENT
E. COVETOUS
F. DISTINGUISHED

17

18

FOND MATES SALT JAM is an anagram of what three-word phrase that means wreckage?

What number in the grid below is two places away from itself multiplied by five, two places away from itself minus two, four places away from itself doubled, three places away from itself plus five, and two places away from itself divided by two.

19

13	46	12	16	20	38
23	16	6	24	22	8
3	7	4	1	30	9
4	2	50	40	8	76
15	90	6	18	2	11
10	14	5	8	20	28

A word can be placed in the brackets that has the same meaning as the words outside. What is it? Each dot represents a letter.

20

OFTEN (• • • • • • • •) HAUNT

Which of the following words is opposite to REFINED?

21

A. UNCOMFORTABLE
B. GAUCHE
C. BRITTLE
D. LOUD
E. ANNOYING

22

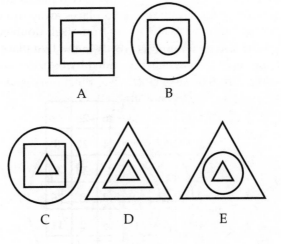

A   B

C   D   E

Which is the odd one out?

Complete the six-letter words so that the last two letters of one word are the first two of the next and the last two of the fifth word are the first two of the first.

23

(• •) M O (• •)
(• •) R I (• •)
(• •) S I (• •)
(• •) V I (• •)
(• •) T H (• •)

Which of the following has the same meaning as SUPPLICATION?

24

A. OVERNIGHT
B. REQUEST
C. ADDITION
D. MOVEMENT
E. CONFIRMATION

Find two synonymous words in the inner and outer spirals of the circle below, one reading clockwise, the other anti- (counter) clockwise. What are the words and missing letters ?

25

What is the meaning of an OREAD?

A. A MOUNTAIN NYMPH
B. A PRECIPICE
C. A PLAIN
D. A CLOCK
E. AN OBSERVATORY

26

What is the decimal value of x in the following sum:

$$7/8 + 7/12 - 5/6 = x$$

27

Which of the following anagrams is not a BIRD?

A. LIGWATA
B. KYSRLAK
C. RAWSOPR
D. THANOZI
E. GONEDUD

28

MENU MASCOT is an anagram of what 10-letter word?

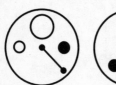

Which of the circles below should replace the question mark above?

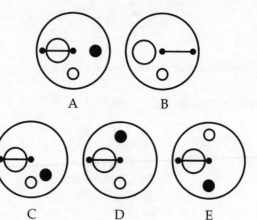

30

A   B

C   D   E

Which two words are the closest in meaning?

A. MASQUERADE
B. MAUNDER
C. MAUDLIN
D. MEANDER
E. MEDIATE
F. MILD

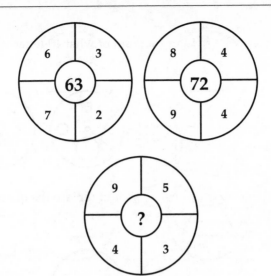

What number should replace the question mark?

What is the name given to a group of WRITERS?

A. CLATTER
B. DECEIT
C. WORSHIP
D. POVERTY
E. ELOQUENCE

Which of the following is not a drink?

A. ANISETTE
B. FLUMMERY
C. MUSCATEL
D. EGG NOG
E. GRENADINE

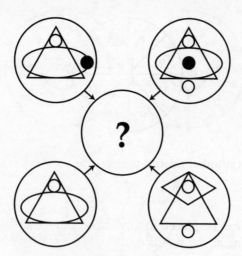

Each line and symbol that appears in the four outer circles, above, is transferred to the middle circle according to how many times it appears, as follows:

One time — it is transferred
Two times — it is possibly transferred
Three times — it is transferred
Four times — it is not transferred

Which of the circles below should appear as the middle circle?

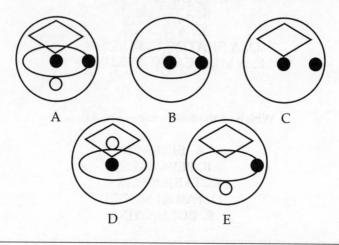

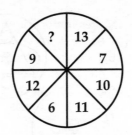

36

What number should replace the question mark?

37

A word can be placed in the brackets that has the same meaning as the words outside. What is it? Each dot represents a letter.

A TREE (• • • • • •) A COUNTRY

38

What is a PILAFF?

A. A TURKISH DISH
B. A WEAPON
C. A DANCE
D. A SKATING MOVEMENT
E. A MUSICAL INSTRUMENT

39

Which of the following is not a dance?

A. BEGUINE
B. PERCALINE
C. TARANTELLA
D. FARRANDOLE
E. POLONAISE

Each of the nine squares in the grid marked 1A to 3C should incorporate all of the items which are shown in the squares of the same letter and number, at the left and top, respectively. For example, 2B should incorporate all of the symbols that are in squares 2 and B. One square, however, is incorrect. Which one is it?

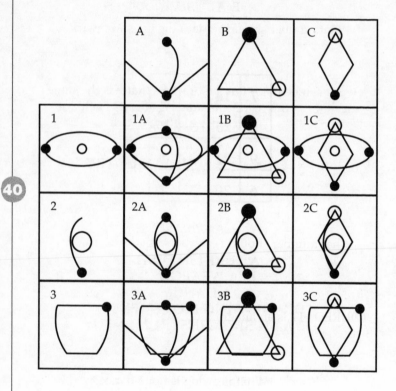

40

Which two words are the closest in meaning?

41

A. MAGNIFICENT
B. VITUPERATIVE
C. SOLEMN
D. DEFAMATORY
E. BRISK
F. ABUSIVE

42

7	14	3	7
8	23	5	17
9	21	3	6
6	20	5	?

What number should replace the question mark?

43

TOURED FIT is an anagram of what nine-letter word?

What is a PUNKAH?

44

A. A FISH
B. A SMOKING IMPLEMENT
C. A FAN
D. A FERN
E. A SERVANT

Each of the nine squares in the grid marked 1A to 3C should incorporate all of the items which are shown in the squares of the same letter and number, at the left and top, respectively. For example, 1B should incorporate all of the symbols that are in squares 1 and B. One square, however, is incorrect. Which one is it?

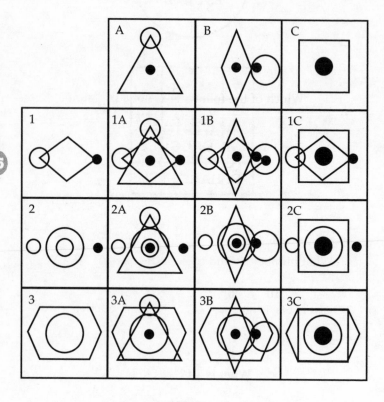

45

What number should replace the question mark?

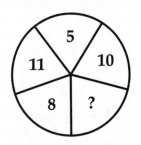

46

Which of the following is not a weapon?

47

A. ESTOC
B. DRUGGET
C. SHAMSHIR
D. HARQUEBUS
E. TEGA

What number should replace the question mark?

48

1   10   26   ?   87   136

What is a COLLOP?

49

A. A SLICE OF MEAT
B. A MEDICINE
C. A BLOW TO THE HEAD
D. A DUSTBIN
E. A MEDAL

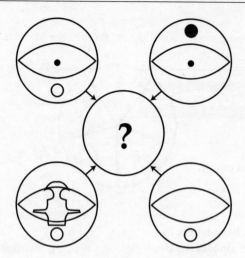

Each line and symbol that appears in the four outer circles, above, is transferred to the middle circle according to how many times it appears, as follows:

One time — it is transferred
Two times — it is possibly transferred
Three times — it is transferred
Four times — it is not transferred

Which of the circles below should appear as the middle circle?

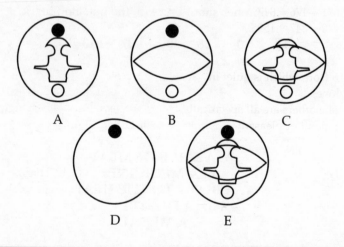

Answers

1 Native and ethnic.

2 D (fist).
All words have letters in the correct alphabetical order without repeating.

3 1595.
Reverse the digits and add it to the original to make the next number.
31 + 13 = 44; 44 + 44 = 88;
88 + 88 = 176;
671 + 176 = 847;
748 + 847 = 1595.

4 B (soft, which is quiet in tone).
The others are all specifically tuneful or pleasant.

5 D.

6 Manipulative.
The missing letters are, reading from top to bottom, P, T, and V.

7 D. The others are exactly the same figure rotated.

8 Improvidence.

9 148.
Reverse the digits in the outer numbers and add them together.
74 + 13 + 61 = 148.
The others are
12 + 23 + 41 = 76;
51 + 26 + 42 = 119.

10 Heroic.
The letters are: stoutHearted, fEarless, intRepid, dOughty, valIant, Courageous.

11 A (large, which is big).
The others mean general.

12
B (drum).
A tambour is a type of drum as a clavier is a type of piano.

13
5.5.
The sequence is:
÷ 3, + 3, x 3, – 3.
1.5 ÷ 3 = 0.5; 0.5 + 3 = 3.5;
3.5 x 3 = 10.5; 10.5 – 3 = 7.5;
7.5 ÷ 3 = 2.5; 2.5 + 3 = 5.5.

14
End, to make offend and endanger.

15
40 mph.
180 miles at 40 mph =
4 hours, 30 min; 180 miles at 45 mph = 4 hours.

16
G.
Reading across columns and down rows, unique elements in the first two are transferred to the third (bottom or right). Common elements disappear.

17
B (pious) and D (irreverent).

18
Flotsam and jetsam.

19
6.
(6 x 5 = 30; 6 – 2 = 4;
6 x 2 = 12; 6 + 5 = 11;
6 ÷ 2 =3).

		12			
3		4		30	
		⑥			11

20
Frequent.

21
B (gauche).

22
C, a circle is outside and a triangle is in the middle.
The others all have the same figure on the outside and in the middle.

23
ALmoST, STriDE, DEsiRE, REviLE, LEthAL.

24
B (request).

25
Jamboree and carnival.
The missing letters are J and B (jamboree) and N and V (carnival).

26 A (a mountain nymph).

27 0.625. The lowest common multiple of 8, 12, and 6 is 24, so redo the sum as

$$\frac{21 + 14 - 20}{24}$$

$15/24 = 5/8$, which is 0.625

28 E (GONEDUD or dudgeon, a fish). The others are LIGWATA (wagtail), KYSRLAK (skylark), RAWSOPR (sparrow), and THANOZI (hoatzin).

29 Consummate.

30 C.
At each stage the black circle rotates 135° clockwise, the white circles both rotate 90° clockwise, and the dot with a line rotates 45° clockwise.

31 B (maunder) and D (meander).

32 60.
The sums are
(top left x top right x bottom left) ÷ bottom right = middle.
$(9 \times 5 \times 4) [180] \div 3 = 60$.
The others are
$(6 \times 3 \times 7) [126] \div 2 = 63$;
$(8 \times 4 \times 9) [288] \div 4 = 72$.

33 C. It's a worship of writers, oddly enough.

34 B (flummery, a sweet dessert or porridge).

35 A.

36 8.
The sum of all diagonally opposite segments is 19.

37 Brazil.

38 A (a Turkish dish).

39 B (percaline, a cloth).

40 1A.

41 B (vituperative) and F (abusive).

42 10.
Reading across each line, the sums are (first column x third column) – second column = fourth column.
(6 x 5) [30] – 20 = 10.
The others are
(7 x 3) [21] – 14 = 7;
(8 x 5) [40] – 23 = 17;
(9 x 3) [27] – 21 = 6.

43 Fortitude.

44 C (a fan).

45 2B.

46 1.
Start at 11 and read alternate segments clockwise, the sums are – 1, – 2, – 3, and – 4, respectively.

47 B (drugget, a type of cloth).

48 51.
At each stage add 3^2, 4^2, 5^2, 6^2, and 7^2.
$1 + 3^2 [9] = 10$;
$10 + 4^2 [16] = 26$;
$26 + 5^2 [25] = 51$;
$51 + 6^2 [36] = 87$;
$87 + 7^2 [49] = 136$.

49 A (a slice of meat).

50 A.